OVERCOMING CANCER

DEFENDER
CRANE, MO

Overcoming Cancer:
From Despair and Desperation to Hope, Life, and a Newfound Mission

By Lynette Hill
Chief executive editor: Donna Howell

Defender Publishing
Crane, MO 65633

ISBN: 978-1-948014-80-9

Printed in the United States of America.

A CIP catalog record of this book is available from the Library of Congress.

Cover photograph by Aubre Cummings
Cover design by Jeffrey Mardis
Interior design and typeset by Katherine Lloyd

Dedication

This book is dedicated first and foremost to my Lord God, whose breath in my lungs is the reason I live. Every beautiful word from every language in the world could be poured into a dedication to You, Lord, and it would still be insufficient in light of how worthy You are to be praised and acknowledged. I therefore humbly make *this entire book* a dedication to You. From cover to cover, every page is prayerfully offered up as a sacrifice to You, my Lord and King. This story of my miraculous healing points to You with every letter, word, sentence, paragraph, and chapter. May it reach those in need with a message of the powerful healing Your medicines are capable of.

To my husband, John Sosa, who was dedicated to me first: You have lived out our marital vows better than I would have ever imagined you could have when you spoke them twenty-five years ago. You promised to remain by my side "through sickness and in health," though you couldn't have known your commitment would go on to be tested against our greatest fears. Nevertheless, you showed just how faithfully you keep your promises as you stuck with me through the unthinkable. You have always been, and still are, my steady hand, and someone I will love with all my being, eternally.

To my sister, Laura Edwards, RN, BS: Having your love, patience, and advocacy throughout the worst time in my life is something I will never be able to fully thank you for. In your desire to be a nurse all those years ago, God knew in all His wisdom that, decades later, you were going to be the advocate your sister would need to navigate a journey she was not prepared for. Thank you for holding my hand and walking through the valley of the shadow of death with me. You have my eternal love and gratitude.

To my amazing sons, Phillip, Kyle, Adam, Isaac, Daniel, Victor, Jason, and Michael: Life is much better with all of you in it. Your love and support would make any mother proud. Much of the strength afforded to me throughout this journey has come from you, and I believe God knew what He was doing when He blessed me with all of you.

To my baby sister, Mary Hill: I always said that, when I grew up, I wanted to be like you. Out of everyone I've ever known, you put others before yourself so consistently that the selflessness within your heart is unmatched. Words have not been invented that could efficiently explain how much you mean to me. Thank you for being there with me through the worst period of my life. You are truly a treasure, and I love you beyond words.

Acknowledgments

Curtis Rindlisbacher, Attorney at Law; Vivian Rindlisbacher, BA, elementary teacher: Your friendship goes beyond what I deserve. Both of you were there with prayers, encouragement, and meals that were collectively such great support to John and my family during this health crisis. Regardless of your busy schedule, you put so much of your life on hold to tend to the needs of our family. You asked for nothing in return—but if you had, your generosity was such that it would take a lifetime to repay you. The words "thank you" are not enough, so I hope you know I am eternally grateful to you both.

Christine Havens, health science/health educator (retired): We had just met at the beginning of my health crisis when a church group told you of my struggles. Having just gone through your own cancer journey, you knew how important it would be for me to have a kindred spirit and friend to talk to who had faced similar dark times. Thank you for being there through the whole process; sitting outside and talking with me in the sunlight; welcoming my questions, and making sure I knew no question was too silly to ask; and laughing with me over potentially awkward (and insanely personal) comments and inquiries regarding chemotherapy's effect on various body parts and functions! All of those conversations, phone calls, and visits made more of a difference than you'll ever comprehend. Your humble servant's heart sets an incredible example of how we should *all* serve others, and I am grateful for that lesson.

Patricia and Candace Holt, mother and daughter: In the twenty years I have known you both, there was never a time I didn't feel love emanating from you—ever. When I started this unfamiliar journey, faced with having to navigate a serious health crisis, you were both there every second of the way. You were always willing to say a prayer with me. There was no limit to the encouraging words you spoke, and you always wholeheartedly believed I would overcome this, because you "didn't want to imagine a world without me in it." I love you both for your unfailing faith and help during my journey.

Ann Armstrong, graphic designer: You are the friend that everyone needs. You have the boldness to tackle the hard and uncomfortable, but necessary, questions that nobody else knows how to approach, such as: preparing a will, making sure it's updated, getting account passwords safely into the hands of loved ones, and generally having all affairs in order. For this and many other reasons, when the winds of life were blowing uncontrollably, I knew you were the steady hand that would never let go. You sat by my bedside while I looked a total mess and you never cared. The warmth of your eyes in those hours, so full of concern; when you said you loved me, I had already known it to be true. Thank you for being my friend.

And finally, all my prayer-warrior partners in so many parts of the world: God heard my name in His ears so often, and as a result, He guided me toward His medicine, which was what ultimately healed me. For this, you have my sincere and eternal thanks.

April 2023, restored to health and surrounded by my tribe: Candace, Patricia and Christine

October 2022, going to dinner with John (in back) and true friends Curtis and Vivian

Contents

Foreword

By Joe Horn—Board Certified Holistic Health Practitioner, fitness and nutrition specialist, and bestselling author of *Timebomb*

In the fabric of human history, the strongest threads that bind us together and renew the faith we place in ourselves and our fellow man are often born from the blood, sweat, and tears of humanity's grandest heroes. Once in a while, a true story emerges that is so incredible and powerful it cannot be left untold, lest we risk tipping the balance: If we ever stop celebrating the accomplishments of the most remarkable among us, we may become emotionally catatonic and incapable of positive change, because in many cases, it is the hero's story that can effectively motivate us toward improvement. I can't think of a more deserving candidate for wearing the "hero" nametag than Lynette Hill, whose testimony is not only inspiring for every reader, but quite literally has the power to change lives, permanently and positively.

In this fast-paced, contemporary world marked by rapidly increasing technological advances in science and medicine, we as a people have traded some of the most basic, foundational concepts of health maintenance and self-care for flashy prescription bottles marketed as "quick fixes" for every fathomable ailment. Never in our shared history have we had so many hundreds of thousands of medicines, treatments, and alleged "cures" believed to heal us and restore us to optimal physical health and function…yet many of us have *never been more sick or vulnerable to disease.* It pains me to see many precious people carrying disease in their body that they simply shouldn't have to carry. So often, these conditions could be corrected through a few changes to the toxins people put in their bloodstream on the daily, but we are instead made to believe the condition is a genetic disorder or equivalent, and therefore, there is nothing we can do but learn to live with disease while we attempt to mitigate the severity of the symptoms through *pharmakeia*.

But again, once in a while, a hero comes along to challenge the status quo and remind us all that we are capable of so much more! Through this book you hold in your hands, Lynette Hill has done that and more in spades: In the face of a stage-four, "incurable" breast cancer diagnosis that guaranteed her imminent death (according to the world's mainstream narrative), Lynette smashed through the barriers of expectation! In an act of unparalleled bravery, she followed a prompting of God to set all other treatments aside and turn to *His* medicine, the natural herbs and plants of the fields that *He* made, to rescue her from death's grip and bring her into the fullness of His restoration. Both God and His medicine delivered, and Lynette is a walking testimony of the potency of the rich healing properties intrinsically stored within the same herbs and plants of the field that God made for the benefit of humankind (Psalms 104:14).

And while I applaud Lynette for her bravery, my endorsement of this book is about *far more* than celebrating a hero. I pray to see a copy of this book in the hands of every person who feels the sting of hopelessness in their own medical health situation. Lynette's harrowing journey is a testimony of healing I sincerely believe is meant to reach the hands of millions of readers, because the outcome of her story *is not exclusive to her*. The prayerful steps she followed in the midst of her darkest hour from man-made medicines to God's is a true inspiration for countless others who possibly stand to see a similar outcome. As Lynette points out, God made the human body to self-heal, and that applies to all of us.

I pray you find both inspiration and healing in the pages of this book.

Introduction

TWO SIDES TO THE CANCER STORY

As long as I live, I will never forget the surreal disconnect between feeling perfectly fine one minute, and in the next, being warned I had better get my affairs in order because, in "months," I would be gone. I still recall the events that played out as lucidly as one perceives their reflection in a clean mirror: no fuzzy lines, no blurring—every detail flawlessly crisp as I faced the Western cancer treatment protocol.

It starts with the picture of bad news, sitting on the edge of the bathtub, clutching a towel to my face, asking every hard question someone could think to ask regarding what it's going to be like around here for my husband and kids once I'd become "the dearly departed." It morphs into the image of chemotherapeutic decay: my skin scaley and rashed, like a burnt snake; mouth sores preventing me from eating and drinking or speaking normally; a head full of formerly gorgeous hair, now dull, falling off in sickly chunks; and my body aging decades overnight, becoming skeletally thin, haggard, and discolored, like an old, withered nicotine stain on legs... But all of that pales in comparison to the snapshot of the dementia-like disorientation, delirium, and dizziness blasting me right before I die...without being given a chance to say goodbye.

Of course, I remember it all quite coherently. I'll never forget *any* of it. And who are we kidding? God would never allow me to forget a single moment.

Why?

Because *He* has a treatment protocol, too, and it's the only reason I still draw breath:

Though I will always recall the river of bitter tears I cried when doctors informed me my life was over, I will also recall the river of joyful tears

I cried when God then informed me my life was just beginning, as His medicine would do what mankind's could not.

Certainly, I will continually harbor the memories of the unadulterated agony and pain brought about by chemotherapy, but I will likewise continually harbor the memories of the unadulterated relief and rest brought about by the Lord's natural therapies.

And sure—I will forever remember the day I died. However, I will also forever remember the day I defeated the grave, rose up from out of the ashes, *and had every single cell restored to my body tenfold* on account of the Creator's medicine; herbs and plants that originate from His soil, capable of bringing about modern-day Lazarus testimonies…of which I am one.

That's why God would never allow me to forget.

Oh, yeah. And one more thing: Because He wants me to tell *both* sides of the story.

Regarding cancer, there's the mainstream, Western side: For many who experience this path, they feel overwhelmed by what appears to be frantic volleys of medical intervention, they hear stories about countless fatalities, sickness and misery in abundance, and statements of resignation as doctors and nurses whisper "there's nothing more we can do" into the ears of the already hopeless. In fact, in my opinion, the Western cancer narrative is *so* associated with certain death that the first question that comes to mind when someone receives a diagnosis is often, "How much time do I have?" Many times, it doesn't even cross a person's mind to question whether survival could be a part of their testimony. Meanwhile, that elusive word "remission" everyone prays to hear can be replaced with the word "recurrence" at any moment after that, painting a bleak portrait of cyclic despair, indeed.

It seems that almost everyone in our area of the world has had their lives touched by a cancer case in some way or other. We live with and around such highly-processed and toxic foods, cosmetics, hygiene and cleaning products, etc., and the majority of the labelling games we play insinuate these items *could* contribute to cancer, sure…though "not in moderation." And of course, that's fine, until *all* the products are given an allotted allowance of toxicity, and "moderation" is a joke: when everything is "just a little toxic," then collectively, the world around us is just a tumor waiting to happen. Then we get to the dreaded chemotherapy—a "fight poison with poison" approach where a manmade, lab-created drug goes after and kills the cancer cells, wiping out the body's healthy cells in the process.

My heart breaks. I love the *people* in the Western system, and I always will. I don't question their motives to be anything less than heroically pure. But my heart breaks for folks on both sides—the treaters and the treated—who don't know it may not have to be this way.

I'm eager to tell you: There *is* another side to the story. It's one that begins when the Creator of the universe gathered dust, breathed life into it, and made the first human with a bulk of biological mass called a "body," *which is capable of healing itself*, assuming the proper conditions to do so are met. Providentially, the Creator also formed the biosphere for the benefit of humanity, and within it, the very plants capable of bringing the human body back to its optimal, self-repairing state, should it become injured.

When I was diagnosed with cancer, I went straight into the Western system, because, unlike the position you readers will be in by the end of this book, I didn't know there was another side to the story. Nobody told me the cancer-fighting herbs and plants God made nearer to Earth's birthday are still here, still thriving, and still waiting to make His people thrive. (Most people simply don't know, for reasons I will discuss later on.) Unlike the vast majority of cancer patients, I got to *live* both sides of the story.

...And I've written this book to tell you about the winning side.

Cancer has its own plan.

God has a better one.

Chapter One

A "FIBER DEFICIENCY"

Neo, my eggshell-white, purebred German Shepherd (named after the hero from *The Matrix* franchise), loved to wrestle playfully. And up until that horrible phone call that rendered me emotionally incapacitated, I loved to wrestle around right back. I have many fond memories of him responding to my voice from the house, running to greet me at the car upon my arrival home, jumping up from his rest on a mound of grass, and trampling anything in his way to reach me as he hears that spirited, light-hearted invitation of mine to stand before me with his tail wagging in anticipation of a good old-fashioned grapple. That's simply how it had always been. But then, without warning, something in his demeanor changed approximately a month before the fateful moment my cell phone blinked to life and changed everything. He just wasn't the same Neo to me that he had been.

One seemingly ordinary day, just like he had done thousands of times before, Neo heard my car pull in from the gate and cross the smoothly paved driveway that made up much of his kingdom—otherwise known as my quarter-acre front yard. As the sound of the motor quieted and the car door swung open, I saw Neo bounding across the lawn as usual, jumping up and down in anticipation of his best friend's homecoming. I reached out to engage in our typical reception ritual: his head in my hands, lovingly tussling back and forth in the air while his adorable back paws hopped about the grass in search of traction.

But this day was different. Something was distracting him. Something was off about his behavior that I couldn't put my finger on. I squatted down to meet him on his level to interact with him further. His tail lowered timidly and he pressed his snout to my stomach, then to my chest, sniffing about the surrounding air erratically.

What's gotten into you, Neo? I thought to myself. *You know you're not going to find any treats on me, right? Silly dog…*

The first few times it happened, I let it go with an internal chuckle, assuming my trusty pal may be showing me a new side of his curiosity he hadn't pursued before. I never imagined for a moment that he was picking up on anything more than the standard bouquet of acidic fruit still lingering in the threads of my blouse from lunch, or an unfamiliar scent I picked up at the airport or a hotel during my out-of-state travels for work. Eventually, however, after repeated air-sniffing around my belly and chest, it became harder to ignore. His futile "search for a treat" remained gentle, but his mannerisms took on a firmly persistent edge, as if he was trying to draw my attention to something specific, and "giving up" was not in his doggie vocabulary. He may not have been a Pointer breed who lifts one leg, straightens his tail, and stares intensely in one direction to mark prey or small game for a hunter in the woods, but he was "pointing" to something in his own way, and he wasn't letting it go.

By the time he began laying his head soberly on my lap and snuggling up against me more than ever in what can only be described as a canine's utmost expression of concern, I knew he was troubled, but I was still miles away from grasping what it was he was sensing. Over and over, I just remember thinking my sweet Neo was turning into a neurotic hound with fantastical ideas of his own.

Maybe he's just getting older, I thought. *Maybe dogs, like humans, just chill out and take on a more mature, rested personality as they age and this is the beginning phases of that transition…?*

I had no idea that dogs could smell various forms of cancer from deeply beneath the skin. What I *was* about to discover, however, was just how meaningful his affection would be a month later when my world crashed to a halt: when I watched everything solid around me turn to liquid and splash to the ground in an explosion of muck without so much as a nod to a past life that was once stable, customary, familiar…and me, weak and trembling, washing downstream like a twig in a flood, swallowed whole and drifting at the mercy of turbulent currents. I would welcome Neo's companionship when I was bombarded with the piercingly loud squeal of daily routine and progress screeching to a stop as visits to one doctor after another repetitiously stole my career, my independence…my *life.*

I would seek him out and embrace his calm head on my lap when I felt overwhelmed by phone calls, medical updates, constant examinations, and the obliteration of any personal space.

When the green light of my world changed to a menacing stop sign.

2018, before diagnosis

But there would also come a day soon—far sooner than I could prepare myself for—that I would be too physically weak to greet Neo at all. Those would be the days that he, alongside my husband's dog, Roger, would spend a lot of time familiarizing themselves with our gigantic outdoor kennel. My precious husband, John, understood that our dogs were protective of me, so when my home became a ceaselessly revolving door for strange visitors to the sick—or "invaders," as the canine mind perceives—the kennel would become their temporary domicile. And as spacious as that area may be, it still pained me to see our two furry, four-legged family members rolling around in the dirt behind a fence, largely oblivious to what "Mama" was going through when they would normally be right by my side or at my feet amid our daily activities. By the time their typically beautiful, well-maintained, shiny coats lost their luster to a light layer of California dust, I was too weak to shower my own body, let alone bathe the dogs. John, alongside the rest of my family, always made sure Neo and Roger were well-fed and greeted on the daily so they knew they were loved, but when the doctors told my husband I wasn't going to make it, lathering and rinsing dogs took a back seat to remaining by my side in the midst of my storm.

And oh, what a storm it was. Perhaps the single most confusing element to the whole situation was why I ever ended up with cancer in the first place.

I had been healthy since forever. The only times I had ever really been admitted to a hospital was during the birth of my sons, and doctor visits, for me, were as rare as a blizzard in my home state of California. My diet for more than twenty-five years had been strictly vegetarian, and I took it seriously: breakfast omelets made from my own, home-raised chicken eggs, seasoned with a light sprinkling of Himalayan sea salt, cayenne pepper, and turmeric; frequent salad greens with that bittersweet mixture of fruit, left undefiled by even a drip of dressing; the "special occasion" unsalted, slow-cooked beans with a side of Spanish rice—but only in small portions due to the starch content; and similar, radically wholesome choices. It was the kind of diet you see displayed in government-issued nutrition pamphlets that litter the entrance of medical clinics and doctors' offices.

Though it's true I sometimes treated myself to a small, personal lunch-sized bag of potato chips or a cookie (a habit that is now strictly a part of my past), comparatively speaking, the pre-diagnosis choices I made regarding foods were devoutly prudent: beautiful, colorful plants on a plate (broccoli, cabbage, cauliflower, carrots, bell peppers, cucumbers, watermelon, avocadoes, peaches, plums, mangos, apples, etc.) with the occasional cameo appearance from your friendly, neighborhood carbohydrate or vegetable-sourced protein. Health always was a top priority for me, and I didn't mess around. Of every goal I could have given precedence to, a long life under God and with family was the central driving force behind every bite I took. I knew I would only ever have one body and one life, and each depended upon the other to be cared for appropriately. I've recurrently avoided processed foods, and one-ingredient recipes are a common go-to for me. (From the book, *Timebomb*, by Joe Horn, I would learn that much of our "healthy, natural produce" is laden with harmful growth enhancers, herbicides, pesticides, and more. This mind-blowing book also opened my eyes to more efficient interpretation of food labels, loopholes in food regulation, and navigating the local grocery store.)

And though I've never been that girl who's inseparably glued to the treadmills and weightlifting machines of the local gym, I had a decent daily exercise regimen, walking my dogs a couple miles every day, tending to my garden, keeping up with our two acres of land, and finding odd jobs around the house. So long as my body was in motion and I was relatively fit, I felt good about those choices as well: not an obsessive supermodel, but *never* a couch potato, either.

Some readers may get to this point and wonder about my history with over-the-counter medicines or harsh pharmaceuticals, but that, too, is a short story hardly worth mentioning, other than to rule them out as suspects in the search for a cancer culprit. I didn't use pills or prescriptions of any kind, almost *ever*, because I was healthy enough I never needed to and strong enough to power through light aches. There was only one exception: I had struggled with severe migraines years prior that led to an intake of prescription-strength pain meds. However, as soon as I decided to give the vegetarian lifestyle a try and cut meat from my diet, the migraines went away and never returned, so I survived even without the most basic, foundational staples (like acetaminophen or ibuprofen) found in practically every bathroom cabinet in the country. *Twenty years* passed between my last migraine pill and my diagnosis in 2021—all the while dutifully reporting for annual physical exams including regular checks for cancer (Pap smears, mammograms, and so on)—so blaming my entire cancer episode on the marginal number of headache meds I took more than two decades ago is a stretch, to say the least.

With cancer as the furthest thing from my mind in those days, these habits were much of the reason I couldn't figure out what in the world was suddenly going on with my digestive system. I was pretty backed up.

How could a person with such a religiously clean diet have trouble using the restroom? How could lettuce, chopped tomatoes, sliced apples, and the occasional side of rice cause one to become blocked like I was? As of late, my mind had been growing increasingly tired of trying to locate some small shell of an answer as to why I couldn't use the restroom "like normal people."

"Normal people." The words were thick in the air, ever wagging an adolescent "ha-ha" in front of my face, whether they were spoken aloud or not. I had never known how much I appreciated being "normal" until "normal" was a distant memory. Folks all around me were taking advantage of every casual trip to the restroom, emptying their waste without a thought and completely unaware there were those of us who wondered if we would ever visit that porcelain throne again without breaking a sweat. But I had gone from being one of *them* to...whoever or whatever I was now: the lady whose bowels wouldn't budge. I was simply tending to normal life one day, and endlessly staring at the wall in my bathroom without movement the next, despite the high volumes of natural fiber I had recently put in my body.

In the beginning, I had reached out to my son, Victor—a proficiently knowledgeable nurse who passed the state exam in his nursing program with flying colors. Certainly, of all people, he would know what to do...

After hearing my predicament, he advised me to visit my local pharmacy for a colon-cleanse, believing that my health habits couldn't possibly allow for anything worse than a standard (however anomalous) bout of irregularity. And, at first, it appeared to be just that; after administering the cleanse, I was walking on sunshine for the next few days.

But it didn't last.

When the symptoms came back later that week, I decided to get checked out at a nearby urgent care facility. My daughter-in-law, Rose, worked at a doctor's office for a reputable man named Dr. Thomas Bakir. Of course, I believed he could be *my* primary caregiver if it ever came to that, but it was Saturday. My job kept me too busy to mess with a rudimentary constipation issue on the weekdays, so I decided to just tackle this problem over the weekend and get seen right away while I had time. That way, whatever treatment I was placed on or advice I received could therefore be in full-swing by the time I returned to work on Monday.

Of course, as anyone would imagine, there was a slight flush to my cheeks—likely concealed from the public under my dark African-American skin tones—upon having to go see a doctor for assistance in toilet use. (Nobody wants to go tell some random doctor at a walk-in clinic about their unusual restroom troubles. And let's be real: If someone *does* love having this conversation with complete strangers, they would be the exception, and not the rule. Perhaps allowing some wiggle-room grace for, say, a medical student or someone whose drive in life is to know and understand the workings of the human body from a purely scientific and professional perspective, the one who thoroughly thrives on sharing their intimate waste-evacuation predicaments probably needs to see a "different kind of doctor"...but I digress.) Part of me was grateful the facility required masking up as a response to the COVID-19 pandemic because, oddly, it was something I could hide behind.

How embarrassing, I thought with a deep sigh as I pulled the black cloth mask loops behind my ears and tugged the fabric up over my nose and mouth. *Come on, Lynette...get this over with.*

I approached the counter timidly, regretting in advance what I was about to reveal.

"Hello there," the lady behind the clinic counter said in greeting. "How can we help you today?"

"Uh, well..." I looked around, noting the place was packed. So many other patrons—all quietly waiting their turn to see the doctor—stared in my direction, some no doubt wondering if whatever ailment landed me here was more critical than their own, resulting in getting bumped down the list of priority patients as per standard triage policy. Unlike some of them, however, I was walking upright and, from the outside, nothing serious appeared to be wrong with me: no blood, crutches, slings, or bandages; no coughing, red eyes, or exasperated facial expression of pain. I was just your average woman, sauntering casually into a building marked "*Urgent* Care," in the middle of a terrifying pandemic crisis that was instilling fear into the hearts of everyone on the planet at the time, looking about as upsetting as a person nonchalantly ordering a pizza.

I'm here for a legitimate reason, I reassured myself. *All I have to do is state my situation and get past this stupid little bowel thing so I can get back to my life and routine.*

Turning my attention back to the woman behind the desk, I leaned forward a little, hoping my body language would notify her that the reason for my visit was awkwardly personal.

"I can't use the restroom," I whispered quietly.

"I'm sorry, ma'am, what?" she stated loud enough to alert the White House. "I couldn't hear you. What's going on?"

Oh, dear Lord...

The woman may as well have pulled out a megaphone and announced to the room that the reason for my visit was everyone's business. I resisted the urge to glance about the room again to take in the skeptical glances of those who were visibly more uncomfortable than I, but I could certainly feel their eyes drilling holes into my back.

I don't know these people. I will likely never see them again. Who cares if they overhear?

With a shrug, I blinked, stiffened myself for the inevitable embarrassment, and spoke a little louder: "I can't use the restroom. Something is going on with my body. I can't…uh, use the toilet."

After a nod and some shuffling about, the lady produced some paperwork on a clipboard and muttered a few instructions for filling them out. I made my way to a vacant seat, still resolved to focus on my own issues rather than worry about who may be sharing a chuckle or two at my expense, and set to completing the admission forms. When I was finished, I braved the trip to the desk to hand them in and returned to my seat, eager for the whole ordeal to be a distant memory while I flipped through a few of the facility's waiting-room car magazines.

Tra la la… Pay no attention to the lady looking at cars. There's absolutely nothing of interest to you here, folks.

Surprisingly, they got me in after only a half hour or so. I was led to an exam room where a nurse quizzed me on current symptoms and then carried out the usual pre-exam routine of taking the patient's vitals. Upon her departure, I relaxed a little, glad to be in the privacy of my own company while I waited for the doctor. A towering, Caucasian man in a lab coat arrived minutes later, entering after a brief courtesy knock.

"Lynette?"

"Yes," I answered with a nod and a timid smile.

He introduced himself and took a seat opposite me, launching directly into what would prove to be a very short initial investigation into the cause behind my blockage. I could tell from the number of patrons in the waiting room that he was slammed, so I didn't take it personally when he was so straight-to-the-point in his nature. Apart from his speed, his bedside manner was gentle and kind.

"So, you're having some problems using the restroom, I hear?"

My eyes drifted to the white tile floor for a second or two, but in the interest of getting past the humiliation of it all as fast as possible, I forced myself to lock eyes with him and face the issue head-on.

"Actually, I haven't had a bowel movement in several days," I explained.

"And that's not normal for me. I have never had a problem like this before." I recounted my usual diet, making sure he knew that I had an above-average intake of fruits and vegetables (and therefore fiber), and then told him about my experience with the temporary relief from the colon cleanse. "I just don't understand why the problem came *back*."

His smile was warm and compassionate as he reached for a pad and started writing up a prescription. "Well, I know it's uncomfortable, but it's also pretty common at your age. Our bodies do change as we get older, and since you're over fifty years old, I would wager it's likely just your body's way of telling you that you need more fiber in your diet. Take me, personally, for instance." He stated the name of a popular, over-the-counter psyllium fiber supplement. "I take it every single day just to stay regular, but considering the gravity of your symptoms, we'll get you hooked up with something stronger."

I waited patiently for him to finish scribbling, even though a part of me suspected there was more to this whole picture than a common, age-induced constipation. As nice as he was, this doctor had no way of knowing just how devoted I was to healthy eating, and something wasn't adding up.

But maybe he was right...?

I glanced down at the paper just in time to see his hand come to an abrupt stop. I'm no prescription-verbiage expert, but even I could tell there wasn't enough information recorded on his pad to direct any pharmacy toward fulfilling a medication. I had been expecting him to hand me the paper, stand, proceed with a cordial goodbye, and then hurry off to his other patients, but that's not what happened.

This turn of events will be preserved forever in my memory as "a God moment," as they say in Christian lingo, because, in my humble opinion, a gut-check from God is the only explanation for why this wise and experienced doctor would second-guess his own diagnosis...

...And it probably saved my life.

His face gradually took on an inquisitive expression—a slight squint accompanied by a knitted brow—and he paused, regarding me thoughtfully.

Oh no, I thought. *Why is he looking at me like that? What is he thinking?*

Turning to his computer, he clicked and typed a few things as his eyes darted about the screen. "Our health network is connected here," he said, "and looking at your medical history, I understand you've never been sick, and you're not on any meds, so *just* to be on the safe side of things, let's go ahead and take some blood to make sure there's nothing else going on. We will send the results to your doctor for follow-up care."

"Just to be safe"... Yeah, that's probably a good idea. I'm sure it will be fine. But ugh! Taking blood is such a pain in the butt with these tiny veins of mine.

Squelching my superficial dread, I nodded and went along with his plan. Minutes later, I suffered what would be the first of oh-so-many bad blood-and-needle torments in the coming year. The poor medical assistant *tried* to draw what she needed for the labs, all the while poking and prodding about the inside of my elbow: squeezing here, pressing there; twisting this, jiggling that; tying, untying, and retying the blue rubber stretch-tourniquet; pumping the arm, making a fist; returning to the first spot—twist, jiggle, squirm, press...nuh-uh; abandoning that idea and going back to the third spot—poke, prod, prick, wait...nope; back to spot two, poke, prod, prick...

Nothing.

Evidently, my veins knew what she was up to and scrambled to hide. Just the smallest dot of blood where the needle had gone in multiple times beaded atop my skin, but this girl wanted enough volume to fill a few lab vials, and she was never going to get it.

I'm a phlebotomist's nightmare. Delivering my boys in the hospital proved that in the past. My veins had a way of disappearing under the surface and, even when they popped up to say hello, it was a teasing cameo-appearance from a petite little line that ran away in laughter if you dared to blink during extraction. That particular part of my story would become an enormous nuisance just around the corner from this appointment.

On the other hand, this particular part of my story would *also* mark the coming year with a profound spiritual lesson: "Remember who to lean on," the lesson would continuously prompt. "Remember who's *really* in charge of your health and your body. It's not mankind."

The young girl released an exasperated sigh. "Hang on," she said, calling another assistant for help.

The second gal surprised me with her approach. Here we were, in a *secular* urgent care clinic, with God-only-knows who believed in what various religions or deities, and she asked to pray to Jesus with me on the spot. I was pleasantly taken aback, but I quickly agreed. Humbly, she got on her knees and took my hands in hers.

"Sorry my hands are so cold," I said nervously. "My hands are *always* cold. It's been that way my whole life."

Her bubbly laugh was as supportive as her beaming smile, and I softened further. I saw her bow her head and followed suit.

"Dear Jesus," she began solemnly. "Give this lady comfort for this procedure..."

I wish I could say I remember the rest of the prayer, but to be honest, I was so amazed by her willingness to turn this blood draw over to Christ, *Himself*, that other than asking for my comfort, I don't recall the rest of her petition, except that it also ended with, "In Jesus' Name, amen."

What I do clearly recall is the subsequent blood draw.

It was flawless: She pulled the stretch-tourniquet, pressed down, found a vein, pricked, and filled the vials, all in a matter of a minute.

Thank you, Jesus, I thought to myself, never imagining just how much that prayer set the stage for the journey ahead. Yet, I also couldn't have imagined the massive amount of gratitude I would come to feel toward the doctor who paused, reconsidered his impulse to write my condition off as a fiber deficiency, and ordered the blood labs that exposed much, *much* more than any of us bargained for—though I wouldn't know it for several days yet.

Chapter Two

THE "SOMETHING" IN MY BLOOD

That very evening, just before closing time at the urgent care clinic, I was outside playing with my dogs when my cell rang out from my back pocket. It was an unknown number, and to avoid the inevitable haggling with a potential solicitor, I nearly hit the "ignore call" icon and went on with my day. Just before I did, however—and for some elusive reason I still don't understand other than to chalk it up as a gut feeling (perhaps a feeling led by the same, and *only*, God who I believe halted the physician in his tracks previously)—I stopped what I was doing and reconsidered. Against my initial instinct, I answered the call and the man on the other end identified himself as the practitioner I had met with earlier in the day.

The doctor, himself, is calling me? I wondered silently. *Normally it's a secretary or assistant that returns calls from medical facilities. This guy is either especially personable in his interactions with his patients, or there's something about that blood draw today that justifies him speaking with me directly.*

Sure enough, after the typical "how you doin'?"-type niceties, his voice became a little more serious.

"You need to call and schedule an appointment with your primary caregiver *immediately*," he advised, "Monday morning if at all possible. Your bloodwork results are showing something abnormal."

For a moment, I started to respond with questions, but he persisted with a stern tone. The gentle and kind doctor I had met hours before was still present over the phone, as I could certainly feel his concern, but his lighthearted character had been replaced with a pressing resolve.

"Listen very carefully. Do *not* wait a month for them to casually pencil you in. This is not one of those times when you can allow weeks to go by while you take fiber powders and carry on day-to-day activities with plans to eventually take care of yourself. Get in right now."

I bounced his words around in my head for a moment.

Surely, if it were something serious or life-threatening, he would tell me. Isn't that how this works?

"What do you mean 'something abnormal'?" I inquired. "What did you find in my blood that you're concerned about?"

"Your primary doctor will go over the results with you further. All I feel at liberty to do at this point is to stress to you that follow-up care is needed sooner rather than later."

Evidently it doesn't work that way.

The reason for his reservation dawned on me then. Medical personnel shouldn't operate outside their expertise lest they risk a malpractice lawsuit, and whatever he discovered in my blood was obviously not within his medical area of mastery to discuss at length. That did *not* mean, however, the finding automatically represented a grave situation. It just inferred that, to protect his practice, he couldn't legally provide any further counsel on the matter.

Yeah. That's all it is.

Admittedly, I was a little apprehensive considering the determination behind his voice. I may not work in the medical field, but I know those folks are trained to know better than to scare their patients by placing calls at unusual times and sounding forceful in the advice they give. So, while I got the message loud and clear that this was no ordinary phone call and I couldn't dismiss…*whatever* this was, the complete and total lack of details from his end hadn't given me enough to panic about either. I made the decision then and there that I wasn't going to freak out until I knew more. Besides, I was still in that "blissfully unaware" zone: Something was clearly in my blood that shouldn't be there, but we would figure it out and all would be fine. I would call and establish a primary care relationship with Dr. Bakir on Monday, take some antibiotics for an infection or something, and be back to work by the end of the week at the latest.

It would be fine…

Wrapping up the call and pocketing my cell, I resumed wrestling with Neo and Roger until John arrived home. In the interest of full disclosure, I greeted my husband with the news from the clinic. His response was about like mine: "Better get that set up on Monday, then.

Meanwhile, I'm sure it's nothing too alarming." We were on the same page, and my sister, Laura, a registered nurse who knew my healthy habits, was in agreement as well. I recall the encouragement she shared on the phone that day.

"Lynette," she said in a supportive tone, "you don't have any signs or symptoms of diabetes, and that would probably be my first concern based on a vague report of a blood test. If it were diabetes, it likely wouldn't manifest in a bout of bowel blockage, either. I assume it's something that *does* need treated soon, or else that urgent care clinic doctor wouldn't have called you, but look at how you live and eat! If it's not diabetes, I'm sure it's some small insignificance—something that'll be fixed with a prescription or two."

That night, I slept as soundly as usual, unaware that there was an element of decay in my blood that would eat me alive; a wicked and malevolent disease creeping through my bones, like sinister, black fingers of pollution and death evaporating every healing white blood cell they touched—clutching, seizing, and tearing the fibers of my being into ribbons of rotting flesh from the inside out. While I had been going about my daily life, deep within my DNA, a dragon of malice had been lying dormant, sleeping for months undetected, gaining strength by the hour, until the day it would suddenly stir, lift its serpentine head, and breathe the lethal breath of fatality throughout my body, down to the very marrow of my bones.

And now...the dragon had awakened.

John and I before the diagnosis

"What do you mean the doctor 'can't get me in for the next three months'?" I asked as politely as I could. "The urgent care guy told me I needed to be seen 'immediately'; those were his exact words. Isn't there something you can do?"

"Unfortunately, Ma'am," the receptionist on the other end of the line said with a tone of polite regret, "as you're not yet a regular patient of Dr. Bakir's, the policy would be to set you up as a *new* patient, and that process would begin with a consultation for your current symptoms. A consultation appointment can take longer than the follow-ups, so he likes to schedule time around that. We just don't have anything open for the next three months, possibly four."

"I understand. Thank you."

Deep breath...

Until this moment, I had managed to remain calm. John, Laura, and I had all three concluded that the abnormality within my blood was unlikely to be much of a threat...but in my more honest moments, I knew very well I wasn't a doctor, I had literally no idea what that indefinable non-revelation from the urgent care clinic could mean for my health long-term, and therefore, it could actually be something serious. Many people throughout time who have received that dreaded medical revelation believed it would never happen to *them*. Such diagnoses as heart disease, respiratory infections, diabetes, HIV or AIDS, cirrhosis of the liver, Fibromyalgia, various inflammatory diseases—and that monster of all monsters, cancer!—"only happen in the movies," or "to bad people," or, generally, to everyone else... But how often do we hear a testimony involving the words, "I never thought it would happen to *me*"?

Survey says? "All the time."

Which of these—or uncountable other conditions I had never heard of and couldn't comprehend (let alone pronounce)—could even be spotted through a routine blood test, anyway?

Again, no clue.

All I knew was what I had been told. This "thing" in my body and blood—whatever that "thing" was—needed immediate attention. I did *not* have "three months, possibly four" to wait for a medical center's calendar to clear. I could tell myself all day long to "stay calm and wait for an opening," and I may even be able to accomplish it if I kept it on repeat long enough, but that didn't change the cold, hard fact that a licensed medical professional told me not to wait. Not this time.

It was early Monday morning—the beginning to another bright week of summer. The gorgeous sun was casting its warm radiance across the lawn, bouncing up from the grassy ground and painting an enviable landscape view from my kitchen window. Just out of that picturesque scene, Neo and Roger were up to their usual happy playtime in the yard while John was in the garage working on one of his various fence or furniture creations. Under any other circumstances, I would be able to appreciate the splendor of the day, but on this particular morning, it was as if the universe was taunting me with its magnificence while I was sick and bloated with my mystery condition. Nevertheless, I did enjoy the wonders of nature from the window. It was a welcome, and pleasantly ironic, juxtaposition to the dark thoughts that were only just beginning to burrow a home within the recesses of my mind.

I was by myself in the kitchen, swirling hot Jasmine tea around against the polished ceramic of my thick-walled mug, thankful to be alone in this moment so I could focus on making my next move. I lowered the tea from my lips down to our light grey Formica countertop, paying no mind to the mellow thud it made on contact, and proceeded to scroll with my thumb through the contacts stored in my phone until I landed on the name "Rose."

If anyone had a chance of pulling strings with Dr. Bakir's office, it would likely be one of their employees—someone on the inside who knew their policies and had been an eyewitness to whatever exceptions could be made for someone in my position—and as it turned out, Rose was on duty at the time. My daughter-in-law, appropriately named after the flower her personality resembled—beautiful, pure, and graceful—was as good a candidate as any advocate on both sides, having been a medical assistant for Dr. Bakir for around four years. Rose had married into my family through my husband's son, but she was as much a daughter to me as any child I could have personally conceived. I imagined her wide, beaming smile in my thoughts as I stood there, barefoot and pajama-clad, and pressed the call button, hoping she was available to answer right away.

"Hello!" Rose greeted jovially.

"Hi, Rose. I know you're working down at the office right now, and I'm sorry to bother you, but I think you'll agree that it's justified. I wonder if you could help me with something..."

She listened patiently as I filled her in on the chief details of the previous weekend that led to my conversation with the receptionist. As I approached that portion of the story, I felt my pulse throb a little harder under my jawline at the anxiety-driving predicament I was in. My eyes locked tensely onto the chocolate-brown cupboards in front of me as I repeated the conclusion to a rather shocked Rose.

"Yes. That's what she said. Three to four months."

"Oh, heck no!" Rose blared in disbelief. "You *are* going to see the doctor immediately! I will call you right back."

The line was cut before I could answer, and rather than to give in to the temptation of negative thinking, I forced myself to take a deep breath and trust that Rose would have influence. It was the best chance I had to follow the advice I'd been given so far. While I waited to hear back, I glanced about the kitchen several times nervously seeking to spot some part of the room that I could pour my uneasy energy into—anything to take my mind off the wait—but, like always, I had cleaned up the night before.

I had always been a fairly responsible housekeeper, in part because a messy house got under my skin. When I walked into one of my own living spaces and saw nothing but clutter and a sprawled mess, it made me feel like the walls were closing in on me. Each item out of place contributed to a restlessness that eventually sandpapered all peace and dominated my psyche until I once again surrendered to the impulse to tidy my surroundings. It was certainly less about impressing people than it was about taking care of my own space and wellbeing. However, it also didn't hurt to have my house in order at all times considering how often family or friends swung by unannounced.

My life in that regard had always been like those television sitcoms everyone watches and thinks is unrealistic: folks just strolling in at any time of day, straight through the front door, tossing purses and coats aside, and making a beeline to their object or person of interest as if they owned the place. That's what John and I preferred, and that's how we knew before we ever laid eyes on a visitor whether they were well acquainted with us or not. Solicitors, door-to-door salesmen or evangelists, charity collectors, political activists, petitioners, or people looking to pass out flyers or pamphlets recurrently announced their "stranger" status by knocking the door or ringing the doorbell.

All of that was about to change. Within merely weeks of sipping that mug of hot Jasmine tea on that stunning-but-otherwise-bloated morning, fate would introduce a new way of living: a monitored front door, restricted company, and a house reflecting owners who were far too busy tending to the sick to worry about clutter.

Meanwhile, I found myself tempted to bite my nails again. I had kicked the habit many years ago, but there, in my spotless kitchen, I was fighting the temptation to chew them back to the quick until they bled.

It *felt like* an hour at least, but in reality, Rose called me back within minutes. The wind-chimey melody springing from my cellphone mercifully jerked my attention away from my fingernails and countertops and back to finding answers regarding the beast below my belly.

"I managed to rearrange Dr. Bakir's schedule," Rose announced. "I know it's last-minute, but can you be here by eleven-thirty this morning?"

"You can count on it."

Chapter Three

BUT IT WOULD BE FINE

Still convinced that my condition was menial, John and I agreed it wasn't important he tag along with me to that first appointment with Dr. Bakir. Whereas I had hoped to receive a quick answer—some "Aha! Here's the problem!" line that would fix everything, fluff life's pillows, and allow me to release the pessimistic worries that had subconsciously taken root around the time of that initial "abnormal blood" notice—my meeting with Dr. Bakir was uneventful. It was a joy getting to have my vitals taken by Rose and thank her in person for whatever tricks she performed to get me in right away, but other than that pleasurable exchange, the appointment was underwhelming, and it merely led to several more disenchanting rendezvous with specialists for the next *three solid weeks* before I would have an official diagnosis. Meanwhile, the "not knowing" was worse than any bad news could have been.

Or…at least that's how I felt prior to receiving the news, which, as I would come to learn, was *far* worse than the "not knowing" dynamic. But before I would be graced with the most staggering shockwave of my life, I would be taken for a very bumpy ride, and it would not be *my* hands on the wheel.

First, Dr. Bakir wanted to repeat the blood tests. Like any caring and respectable doctor, he felt the need to have his own familiar circle conduct the screenings to avoid any intercommunication errors between an outside urgent care facility and his office that might otherwise lead to a misdiagnosis. This meant my tiny veins had to be prodded, poked, and pricked all over again. As much as I wish this phlebotomist could have been as lucky as the former—and perhaps she may have been if she would have prayed to Jesus like the last girl did (truly: God only knows)—it did not go well. It was just as I expected: several pokes, blood beading up around the injection site, nothing in the vials, and at least a million apologies from an experienced medical assistant who had never seen the likes of me. Nevertheless, to spare you readers, suffice it to say, they eventually gathered what was necessary to run labs.

Regrettably, the results came back the same: Something flowing throughout my veins and arteries was still ambiguously "abnormal." Dr. Bakir couldn't (or perhaps *wouldn't*) say what the abnormality was until we had run some more diagnostic testing. This would mean more appointments...

Still, I had already known at least that much about my blood, so I was hanging in there for the time being.

The ultrasound Dr. Bakir ordered was carried out a few days later, and it took everything good I had in me to prevent my internal alarm bells from exploding into earsplitting sirens over that experience. The room may have featured serene, dimmed lighting, and the machinery hummed quietly enough that a person need not feel barraged in the same way they would in, for instance, a loud emergency room with endless activity, but despite the tranquil setting, my appointment was unnerving.

After the technician jellied up my abdomen and swirled the wand around for a minute or two, she risked a few very telling glances my direction between images. From the start of the process to the finish, her eyes would bear down on the computer screen in concentration as she snapped a photo and typed a few keys, then down to my belly, adjusting the wand and twisting it in another direction with the countenance of a professional, and then, her eyes would flicker over and lock contact with mine with bullet-in-mid-flight intensity.

Was I imagining this?

Snap, swirl, adjust. Snap, type, swirl—

There it was again! And no, I wasn't imagining it.

Her expression was... Well, I don't know *what* it was, actually. It was a look that told a hundred stories at once, and although I'm usually excellent at reading people, this woman's face was a book that couldn't easily be read. The words were there—whispering...gently mumbling...and then *screaming* to be spoken—but they remained under the surface, obscured by her resolute silence. She had a way of saying a lot of things with those eyes while keeping her mouth sealed. With a mere gaze in my direction, she communicated volumes—and nothing—all at once.

Was that caution or pity behind that stare? Sympathy, perhaps? Concern? Resignation? What *wasn't* she telling me?

"What's going on?" I mustered the boldness to ask. "What are you seeing on there?"

She paused, regarded me thoughtfully, and then donned the mask of professionalism.

"I'm not at liberty to give any opinions as I am not your doctor," she offered with compassionate reservation. "He will have to be the one who goes over the results with you. I'm sorry."

Of course, I wanted immediate answers, and of course, it wasn't her place to give them. I knew that, and yet, it didn't change my deep, earnest yearning for her to just break protocol and spill her cup of secrets so I could understand what was creeping around beneath my own skin.

She didn't spill.

The results took around five more grueling days to get back to Dr. Bakir, who scanned the technician's sonography report and confirmed the presence of an anomalous mass of tissue in my abdomen. Though I'm not an expert, I understand that, generally, ultrasounds only use sound-wave equipment to take pictures of something inside the body. They don't automatically give answers for the causes behind shapes they find, so it's up to the specialists of a given field to analyze what the ultrasound images ultimately convey. In my case, whatever those pictures showed to Dr. Bakir was justifiable reason to run additional tests…which meant additional days of mounting concern.

Yet, the word "mass" was generic.

It's probably just an overgrown cyst, I told myself. *Maybe it's a fibroid that'll just go away on its own. In any case, we'll get it taken care of. It's no big deal. Just a part of life.*

John agreed. "Calm" was the way to proceed. Going from a perfectly healthy life to a scramble of sudden driving all over the county for appointments was highly inconvenient and annoying, but "there was nothing to worry about."

The back-and-forth ping-pong psychology had already begun. Life was good…then something was "abnormal." Life was good again…then I would be the recipient of strange stares during a medical procedure. Life was g—*bam*! Cryptic, unsolved mysteries about a "mass." One minute I was breathing through the nerves and anxiety, praying I would be okay; the next minute I was planning out what kind of apology I would give to my boss and coworkers for my absence when I returned to work "in a couple days." It was in those latter moments that I wished I could throw all these tests and appointments out the window, drink prune juice, use the restroom, and just hang the whole tiresome medical journey on the proverbial "get to it later" billboard in the back of my mind.

Then again, the very appreciation for the fragility of life was what had driven me to stay fit and eat so carefully for all these years, and it wouldn't make sense to be dedicated up to this point just to throw in the towel and neglect my wellbeing. So, as much as the undesirable run-around was bothersome and scary, I dutifully continued to show up whenever and wherever I had been told to be.

The Magnetic Resonance Imaging (MRI) came the following week. John went alongside me, but he was asked to stay in the waiting room. The results of this additional assessment had promised to display a more complete picture of exactly what we were looking at. All I needed to do was wait—*again*—for results. Then treatment could finally be put into motion and I could put all these appointments behind me.

After settling into position on the stretcher protruding from the hole in the MRI machine that this team called "the tube," I closed my eyes, relaxed my muscles, and focused my thoughts upon something pleasant.

The beach, Lynette, I self-directed. *Think of the beach.*

Yep. There it is...

There is no happier place in the world for me than the beach. That ceaseless body of self-undulating waters is a fascinating, thought-provoking enigma: swelling, surging energies rising to a climactic wave that crashes down into deafening ocean sprays; the rise and fall of salt water seemingly on its own; a vast, hulking, massive blue giant with no life essence of its own, yet, paradoxically crawling with hundreds of thousands of marine lifeforms within its own watery mass... And me, standing on the shore like I did back in the day with Grandma on the island Dominica: waves lapping my ankles, the fragrant aroma of the briny depths churning about the air; filling my lungs with the salty scent of God's exquisite creation;

taking in the bright colors of the horizon at sunset; scanning the sand for naturally forming shells or bits of driftwood that travelled from faraway lands carrying heroic tales of their own; and believing that God made all of this just to delight His people, of which I was a part.

I hear you, Lord. Thank you, Lord.

I continued to fill my head with rapture until some beeping and shuffling about pulled me back to reality. The harsh truth I had to face was glaringly apparent: I was *not* at the beach becoming one with earth, sky, God, and Grandma. I was in a cotton gown having my body analyzed with magnets and radio waves.

What a stark contrast.

It would be fine. Just a "mass," whatever that meant. An antibiotic or something would kick it, I was sure. Something like that. Or if not, a quick surgery would remove it. Or…I didn't know enough to guess beyond that, but I was settled on the idea that panic wouldn't accomplish anything, so I kept telling myself whatever I needed to hear myself say to maintain my endurance in the waiting game. The doctors knew what they were doing, and I simply needed to trust the process.

But wow, the word "mass" sounded intimidating! That was starting to mess with me a bit.

But it would be fine. I've always been healthy and healthy people don't just get sick overnight, do they? Surely not…

But my bowel irregularity was obviously more than a fiber deficiency, and didn't that mean something nefarious might be going on!?

But it would be fine. Like the urgent care doctor initially said, it's probably just common, age-related body maintenance.

But this is how a lot of scary stories start, isn't it? Abnormal blood, then a mass, then—

But…but…but… The word was beginning to lose its power of hesitation.

BUT IT WOULD BE FINE!

Ping-pong.

The medical waiting game is not a fun one. I don't recommend it. It has the power to toy with the most peaceful and serene spirit, force the self-assured person into constant second-guessing, break down confidence, and tear down harmonious boundaries set in place for a *lifetime*…

like a wrecking ball from out of nowhere, determined to demolish—no, *obliterate*—the tranquility of the grandest, self-proclaimed Gandhis across the globe.

And I was starting to feel the wrecking ball's momentum.

Trust the process, Lynette. Just trust the process. You'll know soon what all of this means. That MRI will unveil the culprit and all will be well.

Chapter Four

BAD NEWS AND THE BLUE PILL

John and I had been happily married for over twenty years by this time. One of our favorite things to do as a couple together is our nightly routine. Before going to sleep, beginning around seven o'clock in the evening, we head to our modest master bedroom and unwind, which manifests in several different low-key, end-of-the-day hangout sessions: long talks by the open window above our square, marble-top table while I intermittently stare at the precious, custom cedar chest John made for me when we first met; admiring, or tinkering with, the gifts and knickknacks people have bought me throughout the years that I store on my bookshelf; visiting about the events of the day under the gentle breeze of the ceiling fans as we settle into our pajamas... So many priceless moments have been shared between those walls, customarily followed by a dimming of the lights and a TV-watching binge from our cotton-sheet-covered bed. (That is, of course, before the good-natured, fight-for-the-blankets ritual begins—a merry war that has become a running joke between us, though it's based on a true nightly occurrence. John sleeps and steals, I freeze and steal back...and usually he wins. That's the arrangement.)

Typically, John has freshly popped popcorn in his lap for our television time—almost always appearing as excited as a little kid in a movie theater hovering over his buttery treat—while in previous years (prior to my strict adherence to healthy eating) I would snack on regular potato chips.

On this blisteringly hot Friday, July 17, 2021—a date that will forever be etched in my memory—the mood was heavier. Though we chose not to engage in the psychological ping-pong match aloud, it hovered in the air between us like a fog, constantly reminding each of us that the "thing" living in my body was still there wreaking who-knows-what havoc upon my organs.

But it wasn't just a gloomy strain between spouses, and it certainly wasn't only a physical issue.

The "thing" was everywhere and in everything, and it was affecting my thoughts in unusual ways…

The somewhat dated carpet on the floor was light green with flecks of a darker, hunter-green shade peppered throughout. It wouldn't have been my choice (the former owners updated it sometime in the 1980s), but I could find something to appreciate about almost anything in my surroundings. On any other day it might remind the creative optimist of God's earth. But this night, even the optimist would have seen only a sour, retched undertone of sickness—the color of the pale horse from the book of Revelation whose rider is named Death. The darker flecks clustered within the base color may have once held the power to inspire its viewer with thoughts of deeply rich vitamins stored in spinach and other spring-mix salad greens, but this night, the floor looked as though it had been splattered with a putrid witch's brew. My pretty furniture that had always reflected a carefree pastime spent with my best friend in the sunny state of California now posed an invisible, perplexing question mark concerning a future that was in the beginning phases of uncertainty. The table and chairs near the window that had once represented countless hours of lovers' dreaming and planning sat undisturbed, empty, and ready to collect dust as there would be no dreaming and planning there for now. The knickknacks on my bookshelf were all but forgotten, and the large mirror I had walked past so many times, always catching a glimpse of my own cheerful disposition, was now lying to me, showing me the reflection of a woman I had never been—a woman filled with insecurity, confusion, bewilderment, and worry.

Mirror, mirror, on the wall…who is that lady, and what is happening to me?

My happy environment was taking a hit, despite my grandest efforts to hold it all together. Everything I normally took joy in had been contaminated with a coat of doubt, as black and depressing as the plague, and my inner voice that had once been only buoyant and positive was morphing into an unwelcome visitor: whispering, reminding, goading me constantly, "You could be *really* sick, you know…" As much as I tried to slap her away and put Faithful Lynette back in her place, this new side of me, this Fearful Lynette who reflected nothing more than my own worry and anxiety, wouldn't leave. It was as much a part of me as everyone's own cynical inner voice that comes along with mankind's fallen nature, and I am glad to honestly say I have never been plagued with "voices in my head" or any auditory hallucinations. Yet, as any other person who has ever faced tumultuous seasons of life will attest, that "unwelcome visitor" creeping in to blast your peace with thoughts of the worst case scenario is very real. I could successfully suppress her for part of a day, *forcing* myself to trust God, doctors, the process, and positive thinking, but Fearful Lynette's voice was growing louder and stronger.

John chose to forego the popcorn, and there would certainly be no potato chips for me. Not only had I dropped that habit, I had been drinking prune juice like it was going out of style for several weeks by this time, yet "the pipes" still weren't working properly, and I wasn't about to tempt fate by eating anything that late in the evening. In lieu of those missing comforts—which felt needed now more than ever—we resorted to my favorite film of all time, *The Matrix*, as it had always proven successful at taking my mind off reality.

As I nestled under the sheet and into the pillows, affording John a reassuring smile as he roosted in by my side, the monster that had become my bowels roared from under the stomach like a bear awakening from ten straight winters of hibernation: stirring, twisting, stretching, and yawning with a devil-may-care attitude against the walls of the once-peaceful cave he was now disturbing. I willed myself to ignore it and proceeded to press the play button.

There was no use fretting anymore by this time of the evening. The doctors had all gone home for the day. And there likely wouldn't be any purpose in worrying for a good week. Obviously, if the MRI was anything like the ultrasound, I had somewhere in the ballpark of four or five days to psyche myself into a loop—whether that be Fearful Lynette's devastating fear or Faithful Lynette's sincere but timid promises of victory over the "thing" I didn't even know how to pray about—and such endeavors were sure to be futile until we knew more. There was simply no point in thinking or talking about it anymore until we heard back from the doctor. And, if I hadn't heard from him by the middle of the following week, I would start riding whoever I had to for answers. Meanwhile, I was determined to get what I could out of the routine I loved most, and tonight's feature film was sure to deliver.

Ah, my good, familiar escape-friend, *Matrix*. How you comfort me.

Little did I know the film's hero wouldn't even make it to the choice between the blue or red pill—representing the choice between blissful, negligent ignorance in a simulated reality vs. accepting responsibility in the true, but horrifying, apocalyptic reality—before that wind-chimey ringtone of mine would intrude into our evening plans.

The screen of my smartphone lit up, and I was initially annoyed. It was half-past seven o'clock now, and John and I had been through a lot lately. We didn't need solicitors and telemarketers robbing us of what little happiness we could grab onto.

As if in a quick rebuke, the caller ID revealed the name: "Dr. Bakir."

Wait… Why is the doctor calling me at 7:30 in the evening?

"This can't be good," I said forebodingly, shooting a troubled glance at John. "What doctor would call this late? It's *well* after business hours."

John returned my trepidatious stare in silence.

Snapping out of my brief lapse in wonder, I scrambled for the phone, hitting the call-connect button before it had a chance to go to voicemail.

Please be good news! I thought as I hurriedly mashed my thumb down on the speakerphone icon.

"Hello?"

"Hello, there," Dr. Bakir's friendly voice filled the room. "Am I speaking with Lynette?"

"Yes, and John," I notified. "You're on speaker."

"Okay, good. Let me get straight to the purpose of my call. I got the results back from your MRI."

Somewhere near the end of his opening statement, I thought I picked up on an uncomfortable hesitation. His tone went from sociable to mechanical in a split second; from "jolly doctor" to "dutiful messenger"; from a familiar acquaintance over tea to a cop at the door delivering news of a murdered loved one. I played it cool, but I *did not* like the noticeable shift.

"That was fast," I said, not knowing if that was a good or bad sign. "Thank you for reaching out to me at such an hour, Dr. Bakir. What did the tests show?"

Please, God!

I locked eyes with John as the doctor continued. Hope, desperation, and pleading, in their largest measurements, poured from each of us to the other, palpable and thick enough to choke on.

"I… It seems that… Well, Lynette, I'm sorry to inform you—"

No, please no, I thought to myself, feeling what little I had left of a stomach plummet downward. *Don't be "sorry to inform me" of anything. That's never good. Come on, doctor! I need good news!*

I forced myself to hang on his every forthcoming word, despite the strong temptation to tune him out and avert my focus to those ceaselessly teasing "happy thoughts" I tend to champion in times like these. I didn't want to hear what he was about to say, but I knew there was no avoiding it. My muscles tensed as I donned the proverbial "big-girl pants" of lore and allowed the doctor to speak.

"…that your MRI came back, and it shows a twelve-centimeter, cancerous mass around your ovaries. We believe you have ovarian cancer."

I swallowed my gasp for the sake of my beloved spouse, who was no doubt sharing this blow alongside me. I had him to think about, come what may.

"The mass is pushing against your colon, which is why you are unable to have normal bowel movements."

For a moment, I pushed against the creeping, but *welcoming*, sensation to give in to the blackness of a fainting spell. John's face was unrecognizable. His color—usually a handsome, healthy caramel tone characteristic of his Hispanic heritage—was fading into a whitish, ashen-grey, spreading to his ears in a gradation of unadulterated horror. The hope between us vaporized. I was stupefied, and based on the terror stabbing its way into John's sweet features, so was he. In almost thirty years of knowing him so closely, I had never seen him look like this. Despite every appointment, every symptom, every scary word we had heard in the past three weeks, cancer was the last conclusion we would have ever reached.

Dr. Bakir's voice trailed off in a swirling cacophony of medical speak that I was no longer capable of parsing: various nonsensical consonants and vowels that were no longer in a language any human being could understand, blurring and melding together in a jumbled amalgamation of nonsense. Everything slowed to a crawl—seconds turned into hours of brutal panic, aging John and I both a decade under the asphyxiating burden of this blow. The walls of our bedroom began to swell inward, threatening to absorb the oxygen from my lungs and use it to laugh at me. The scarce illumination from the already dimmed overhead lights began to evaporate like mist making way for dominating darkness—an encroaching, unsolicited black phantom assisted by the sun outside the window that had the audacity to descend at this time and bathe the California grounds in slow-creeping shadows. Everything was closing in on me.

Cancer…

The very sound of that six-letter word spoken aloud had introduced a menacing adversary into what had been my safe place minutes prior. My torment was at last identified. My ailment finally branded with a label that held dark power over the flesh. And it was, indeed, an enemy of humanity whose name was synonymous to an irreversible contagion that couldn't be stopped and guaranteed fatality to nearly all whom it touched. Cancer was to human history a silent assailant under cover of the night, slithering about undetected, past all guardians and watchtowers, down grand halls where victims sleep unaware. His steps make no sound, his wicked cackle produces no echo, but the terminal effects of the poison he carries in secret—and the suffering it inflicts upon its doomed target—certifies that his presence will be felt by morning, when the damage he has done is discovered too late. The only way to combat the otherwise lethal properties of this foe's venomous cocktail is to call upon the assistance of a popular challenger known as Chemo to hunt Cancer down and snuff him out…but this contender comes at a high cost, for to utilize him means to inject one's blood with a chemical drug so toxic that it, too, has the potential power of weakness, destruction, and even death.

The devastation was stifling. My environment—*my world*—wasn't just taking a hit, it was collapsing under the weight of a powerful six-letter word and all that it implied. The life I knew only minutes prior was a wreckage of towering bricks on fire, releasing one distress smoke signal after another upwards into a sky that no one was monitoring.

I would have given anything in that moment to go back to *only* being embarrassed about constipation in front of a random group at an urgent care clinic.

The blue pill. I choose the blue pill! I don't care how deep the rabbit hole goes or where it leads. I don't want to see it. I choose blissful ignorance. This can't be happening. I manifest this away. Do you hear me, life!? I MANIFEST this away!

As much as I wanted to reach out and swallow a pill that would cancel this news, I wasn't Neo, and this wasn't the Matrix. The red pill of harsh reality had already been taken, and I was in the beginning of that irreversible journey down the chute to the black world below where my body and mind were about to be unplugged from the comforts of ignorance and obliviousness.

Somehow the called ended, and I found myself instinctively reaching for the remote. The television blinked to black.

Reverse this, God. Give me back my life.

Chapter Five

THE RIVER OF BITTER TEARS

That night, following the fateful call, John and I held each other without a word. Not a single word could have changed fate or benefited us in the whirlwind anyway, so it felt appropriate to allow the silence to carry us into the next morning. It was also glaringly apparent that both of us needed space and time to process such news.

Looking back, I have often wondered how odd it was that I gave into sleep so quickly, that I slept so deeply, and that I didn't dream. I almost *always* dreamed, but this night was just a black blank until I rose to meet another day. Maybe, instead of drifting into rest consciously, in some deeply subconscious attempt to escape circumstances of real life, sleep took me by force and sedated me so efficiently that it rendered me incapable of dreaming. (Perhaps that's what a person does while in shock?)

Slowly, my eyelids parted. I allowed myself a few seconds to confirm in my memory that the events of the previous night were real.

But I *couldn't* confirm it. Not immediately. It was just too unbelievable.

That bizarre transitional stage between sleep and wakefulness didn't usually hold any more power over my logical mind than is normal for folks in that first-thing-in-the-morning fog, but on this particular day, I had to be certain. Scientists had long studied this strange transition-time phenomenon, even assigning it a name: "the hypnagogic state." It was rumored to be a time when the human mind was most creative: between true wakefulness and the slumber that allows the brain to process life in those rapid flash-visuals we call "dreams." Sensory perception—seeing, hearing, smelling, tasting, and feeling touch—could all be experienced as usual, while the mind interpreted those senses from a more flexible, elastic space open to surreal concepts, having just been subjected to one's own internal, illusory, and at times unrealistic reflections. Some of the greatest paintings, musical compositions or lyrics, movie or stage scripts, and numerous other artistic expressions that have become famously iconic landmarks of world cultures have been "unlocked" throughout history while one's mind was in this state. Certain celebrated names throughout history specifically relied on the hypnagogic state—training themselves to tap into that inspiration and take notes immediately on what their mind conceived—such as the composer, Beethoven, or the painter, Salvador Dalí. More often than not, however, the hypnagogic transition inspires reflections that are abstract in nature.

Far be it for me to awaken from sleep and carry into reality the sorrow and trauma of a phone call that hadn't really happened.

Oh, it happened, Fearful Lynette prompted. *That wasn't a dream.*

Did it, though?

As my eyes adjusted to the light, I stared at the ceiling fans. How lucky they were to have been created for such a simple purpose: spinning brown wooden planks in a circle perpetually just to make someone else's existence more physically comfortable. Ceiling fans couldn't feel pain or become constipated. They would never be asked to show up for blood labs, ultrasounds, MRI screenings, or appointments with specialists. No "mass"—cancerous *or* benign—would ever form in their tissues. Nobody would ever expect them to take a phone call and hold themselves together while they learned an incurable disease was ravaging them from the inside out. They didn't have brothers, sisters, mothers, fathers, sons, daughters, friends, or pets whose lives would be flipped upside down by a potentially terminal diagnosis. They were, as the world would see them, "inanimate objects." But from my perspective on the bed below, they were quite animated, showing a life of their own in a never-ending circular dance, predestined to repeat that predictable motion forever as long as the almighty switch on the wall told them to.

John had evidently already risen for the day, as I was alone. Just me and the circular overhead dancers. At any other time, I might have been thankful for my cognitive superiority over these whirling planks, but now, I envied them for their simplicity and appreciated the visual entertainment they provided my tired eyes.

It's pleasantly hypnotic, Faithful Lynette observed. *The way they just keep spinning…*

Don't try to change the subject, Fearful Lynette chided. *This is happening. It's real. You are sick, sick, sick, just like I said you would be—worse, in fact. You have cancer. How long do you think you have to live before—*

I shut my eyes hard and willed my thoughts to stop, even if just for a moment. The light breeze the fans were generating threw cool wind on the fresh tears that plunged backward across my cheekbones and down past my ears to the pillow below. I filled my lungs with air and released it slowly, determined to keep the loud sob in my chest contained until I knew John was out of earshot.

Just breathe for a minute, Lynette, I told myself, knowing that the aggravating and analytical ping-pong match between optimism and pessimism was about to reach a whole new level…if this were, in fact, really happening.

There are so many sayings and phrases in and throughout culture that sound profound when we first hear them. It seems like there's an answer to everything and, if properly applied, these expressions might fix whatever mental anguish we're up against. "When life gives you lemons, make lemonade" for the guy whose car just broke down; he needed to get some exercise walking to the store, anyway. "To err is human; to love is divine" to encourage the woman who feels she can't keep forgiving her husband's poor attitude. "Be the change you want to see" for the young girl complaining about how all her friends behave. They apparently go on and on. A rehearsed, superficial, slap-on, bumper-sticker-answer for every problem in life.

But what verbal Band-Aids exist for the person who has just been informed they have a potentially life-ending condition that the best doctors in the world can't cure? How does *that* person "look on the bright side of life" when life, itself, was just all-but cancelled on them? How do we harness that internal, glorious, God-given, *positive* side of ourselves and utilize it to drown out the voice of our fallen, sinful, *negative* side that thrives on complaining and seeing the bad in everything?

How does Faithful Lynette overpower Fearful Lynette at a time like *this*?

I opened my eyes again. The fans were still turning while my vision blurred under an insufferable surge of silent tears. One by one, they made their salty journey down the sides of my face and plunged into the fibers of my cotton pillowcase—a sudden and never-ending stream of them until I felt the wetness spreading beneath my head—while I stayed perfectly still and quiet. Minutes passed, and there hadn't been a sound from John, yet I couldn't risk him hearing my sorrow from around the corner, and I could feel the bottled-up emotions preparing to manifest in a blast of wailing sobs. I wasn't ready to get out of bed and face…everything I was going to have to face in the coming days, but if I didn't get out of bed in that instant, I was going to lose it.

John deserved better.

I rose and sat at the edge of the bed until I had a solid grip on my balance, and then I slipped into the master bathroom, heading straight for the mirror.

My reflection hadn't changed since the day before. I was still Lynette—proportional, curvy build; brown eyes, only slightly darker than my skin; long, natural African dreadlocks halfway down my back; bright white, well-maintained teeth… I looked the same as I did every other morning, standing there in my t-shirt and shorts like the world was my oyster and the possibilities were endless.

Like I was healthy.

But there was another reality under the surface—a future the mirror didn't have the power to reflect—that thrust its heavy influence back to the forefront of my thoughts whether I liked it or not.

This really is happening, my awakened mind finally accepted. *Last night's phone call from Dr. Bakir was not a dream or a nightmare. It's real.*

And that's when it genuinely hit me.

By God's grace, I'm sure, I managed to stabilize myself into a sitting position on the edge of the bathtub before I surrendered to the colossal explosion of tears and sobs that had been slowly building up in me for those several weeks I had a…"something" in my blood. The deep longing for normalcy, the desire for dependable routine that had planted its seed of doubt in my spirit from the utterance of "abnormality" forward, had grown into a full-blown Redwood Forest pine—towering branches digging into every stable comfort I had ever known—and it decisively pricked my last resolve. Now, I wasn't just emotionally bleeding, I was emotionally hemorrhaging and there was no bandage or tourniquet in the world that could stop the flow. As soon as the flood gates were opened, it gushed, relentlessly.

Was God punishing me? Was it something I had done? Had I made too many wrong decisions in my life and this diagnosis was merely what I deserved? Was this cancer, like so many Christians in recent decades loved to preach, because I had some "hidden sin" I had failed to own in my secret confessions?

Weeping.

...Was God even *there*? For real? This could not and should not be happening to *me*. I had faithfully cared for my vessel for years, upholding standards of health completely ignored by many in our Western culture who were going about their diets and exercise with utter abandon, yet *they* weren't facing this. Why weren't all those biblical statements, these reassuring passages that history's finest preachers repeatedly called "promises of God," keeping me from this outcome? It's not as if I had endorsed the idea that God was a formula. He was far more than some "say/do this and receive that" recipe. I never expected that I could observe some ritualistic act of piousness that God would honor by spitting out expected blessings. Certainly, some followed God that way, but to me, the Lord was not a vending machine, and I knew His ways are not our ways and His thoughts not ours. The book of Isaiah said as much, and I had believed it. But *this*? Surely, I didn't deserve *this*, did I?

Sobbing.

Are you there, God? Fearful Lynette asked.

"I'm scared," I said aloud between uncontrollable, shuddering moans. "I'm so, *so* scared, Jesus!"

Fearful Lynette—which, even in my darkest hour, I knew was nothing more than the weak human in me—was getting louder.

How long did I actually have? The dichotomy of my own natures were warring, and the volume was overwhelmingly shrill. My chest heaved. My lungs convulsed. My fingers gripped the edge of the bathtub like a vice as I continued to let flow every grieving tear...and it *was* absolute, undiluted grief I was expelling.

Grief of a mother and grandmother.

Would I be there for my three-year-old granddaughter's entrance into high school? Would I see her dress for prom? Would I be there to greet my thirteen-year-old grandson who was moving back to California? Who would be mother to my sons? Who would be the mother-in-law my precious grown children's spouses could lean on during moments when Mama's opinion is needed? How many more of my children's birthdays would I see? Oh, dear God… How many would I *not* see?!

Wailing. Howling.

Grief of a wife.

What would become of John? Who would ever be able to appreciate his woodwork the way I had? Who would tease back and forth about who made the best enchiladas? Who would look out for him, help him keep an eye on his own health, or be there in case of emergencies? Who would assist him with Neo and Roger's food, water, hygiene, and playtime? Where would he turn for the friendly camaraderie I had always provided each night with popcorn and movies and dreaming and talking and joking and laughing and commenting about knickknacks? Would the sound of my bubbly laughter echo off the walls of our empty bedroom in mere months from now, reminding sweet John of all he had lost?

Bawling. Groaning. Gasping. Bawling again.

Grief over a life cut short.

Would I ever make it to the beach again to feel the sand between my toes and watch the waves foaming at the edge of the docks? Had I forever missed my chance to go to Yosemite or Yellowstone national parks? To go snorkeling among the dolphins and whales? To go sailing or explore a cave? To go skydiving, bungee jumping, ziplining? To see the Northern Lights in person? Was my time spent in those fascinating Bible studies over for good? Would the last look on the faces of my friends and neighbors be an expression of pity instead of the smiles I had always anticipated? How many sunsets would come and go before my time was up?

Roaring. Panting. Shaking.

Grief over what was still to come.

Would the horrors of chemotherapy be as bad as I'd always heard? Would I be sicker than a dog for weeks, months, or even *years* just to turn around and surrender my life early anyway? Would it be worth it in the end? Would I even be a good candidate for chemotherapy? Or would it be some kind of radiation thing? Was I going to be strong enough to carry myself to and from the bathroom in the coming days? How bad was all of this really about to get?!

Screaming.

Grief of every imaginable kind—and an endless list of questions nobody on this earth could ever provide all the answers for—all hammering and thrashing about my mind in a chorus of commotion and disarray.

The second-hand on my lifespan-clock was mocking me in its own *tic, tic, tic*, counting down evermore in a cruel contrast to my sobs as I spun an entire tapestry of misery and heartache in a single sitting. I cried so hard, so loud, and for so long, wondering what every proper health decision—what every "good person" choice I'd ever made—had accomplished in light of this.

Some people have said they "cried a river of tears" in their darkest hour, but the salty Pacific Ocean had nothing on me. I didn't know until then that I was even capable of producing so many tears, yet the soaked towel I had at some point mindlessly gripped and held against my face proved otherwise. Adrenaline rushed through my diseased veins, pumping my muscles with hysterical urgency, though there was nothing to do and nowhere to go but to sit there and confront a new, profound, and immeasurable dread. My fight-or-flight response system was in full throttle, telling my body to get up and go, to do something about this, to fix it, to intervene in some way, to take measures that would reverse it all and bring a stop to…

…To my own death.

I sat there, alone, lonely, terrified, and shaken. I shook for several minutes while the last fragment of energy within me fought to subdue the ruthless, wracking sobs. Fearful Lynette had overpowered me while my defenses were down. And now, after the grandest demonstration of emotional pain I had ever exhibited, I was defeated.

Under no circumstances did the wild storm of thoughts decrease. That wouldn't happen for quite some time. However, my body was weakening, and I felt it to the marrow in my bones. I couldn't cry like this forever. Nobody could.

Chapter Six

ALLIGATOR SKIN AND THE RED PILL

Slowly, the torrent of lamentation diminished from booming screams to resigned wailing, which continued to ease into short, whimpering moans between tremulous, broken bursts of drawn breaths... As the minutes on the clock continued forward, my cries slowed to lengthy vocal sighs in an attempt to bring the volume of air in and out of my lungs under control.

Breathe in. Breathe out.

Just BREATHE. Like they say on TV: in through the nose; out through the mouth. Get ahold of yourself, Lynette.

Hyperventilation would not improve this, or any other, situation, but with the urgency pulsing through my body—desperately looking for a whole-body-and-spirit release all at once—I had to do more than just think about staying calm. I had to intentionally manifest into the physical what the psychological knew was best: be still, compose, collect, relax. For whatever good it had done me, I had effectively uncapped all I had been bottling up and poured it into a puddle, but I knew I had to be strong for this upcoming journey, and there was no time like the present to at least try to pull myself together, get up from the edge of the bathtub, and move on to whatever came next.

May as well brush my teeth and get ready for the day, I thought.

I took one final deep breath and released it while standing to my feet. After assessing my balance and ability to walk responsibly, I surrendered to my programmed routine of getting ready for the day and walked to the mirror.

There's no point in putting on makeup today. Mascara and lipstick are for people whose days go differently than those I'm living right now.

Reflexively, I turned the faucet on, squeezed some paste onto the bristles of my toothbrush, ran it under the water, and began scrubbing my pearly whites as usual. Fearful Lynette sprang into action again, but this time, having just fed her appetite for a mountain of worry and pessimism, my storage tank of negativity was bone-dry, and my encounter with her would be cut short.

What are you going to tell your family? How are you going to break the news? What if—

Stop! Faithful Lynette intervened quite suddenly. *Just stop. I've had enough of you. I can only take so much. I'm serious. Shut up.*

As I kept my toothbrush in motion, my eyes locked with those belonging to the girl in the mirror: Who was she *really*? Was she a fighter or a coward? Would she ultimately be a lasting survivor or a perpetual victim? Strong or weak? Champion or failure? Productive or self-destructive? Confident or self-loathing? Fruitful or useless? What would her testimony be in the coming months? One that appreciates and treasures God's blessings in this life and salvation in the next? Or one that takes all of that for granted? And which of those two alternatives did she honestly, *truly* want her story to be, regardless of the supreme outcome? The "Christianese" answer was certainly the former option of the two, but it was easier said than done. When real crud hits the fan in this life, if we're *honest*, there are times we prefer to wallow in self-pity and accomplish nothing because it takes far less effort. However, it also doesn't inspire anyone to be better, which is what Christians are called to do. The strongest people throughout humanity's history can be commended for their heroic, unshakable determination and bravery, but they didn't get there by whining. The path to true victory and triumph over almost anything we can possibly face begins with making a fixed, steady choice to overcome, and then committing to uphold that standard come what may.

What would the woman in the mirror choose?

What metal are you really made of, Lynette? I asked myself, bristles rotating. *You've been a sturdy, devout daughter of the Almighty King whose attitude and outlook reflected faith and trust in His ways almost every moment of your life. Now—when it counts—are you going to give in to floundering and jumping into your own grave before it's even dug? Do you, or don't you, still have that alligator skin that you've been so proud of all these years?*

Ah. My "alligator skin."

That took me back… Though nearly everyone has seasons of life that are daunting, I had allowed those moments in my own story to fortify me.

I was born on the small island of Dominica. When I was only six months out of the womb, my biological mother dropped me off at my grandmother's house to be cared for. This way, my mother could look for a better way of life to bring me into at a later time, which was a common practice for the locals there. I had a perfect childhood under the guidance of my grandparents, who I believed to be my real mom and dad. (I used the terms "Grandma" and "Grandpa" regularly, but I wouldn't know those words were not what one calls a direct parent until years later.) Every textbook peace-and-stability element that one might wish for a child to experience was available to me in constant abundance: My grandfather loved my grandmother fully, and doted on her every need, providing an excellent example of what a marriage should be; my house—which was "on the ocean" in a very literal way as it had been built upon stilts merely a few feet above the rolling tide—was a place of beauty, affection, and support; my childhood was filled with laughter, the beach, trips to church where the teachers spoke Latin, attending a Catholic school in uniforms, making octopus soup with Grandma, enjoying fresh air and nature, and taking in the splendor that God personally made in every direction… I couldn't have been happier.

Then, when I was six years old, the confusing day came when my biological mother collected me and took me away to "America, the land of milk and honey." I didn't care about milk, or honey, or any other vague promises of a life I'd never known. I only knew that the life I was living at the time was blissful and fortunate, and anything that threatened that was nothing less than terrifying. In a single instant, I went from planning my next barefoot seaside adventure to being thrust into the care of a woman I never knew existed—torn dramatically from the family and "parents" who had loved and cared for me for as long as I could remember. To this day, I can recall screaming in protest all the way to the airport. My birth mother warned me that if I didn't stop my tantrum, they wouldn't let me on the plane. I prayed she was right and kept up the spectacle, but it didn't work. From paradise, to plane, to this foreign land called "America," I was thrust into a whole new world.

The relationship I had the privilege of observing between my grandparents was nothing like what would be lived out around me in my new home. My birth parents were as human as any others, and therefore subject to past mistakes that I would never want them to feel forever accountable to apologizing for, but suffice it to say that I would not be in a loving environment again until I married John. The canvas of bright, calming colors that had been my childhood was quickly doused in paint thinner and layered with dark shades of angst and apprehension over nearly every move anyone made in that space. The ground upon which I then stood was paved in disorder and instability, no reliable footing to be found, like a tightrope with circus clowns rattling the line at each end…and me, in the middle, terrified to look down and realize there is no net to catch me if I fell. It was *not* a happy place, and the disconcerting events I witnessed broke me deeply. I learned to sleep very lightly as a little girl because I never knew what was going to blow up around me next. Trials abounded for many years, forcing me to abandon all expectations and take life in strides, one day at a time. Moments that the average youth looks forward to—prom, school functions, family days, parties, potlucks, and the like—was fictional to me. Instead, I learned to bury my nose in a book and plead with God that each day would be uneventful.

To add insult to injury, the culture in this new "milk and honey" country was, at that time and in certain cities, horrible for a colored girl. I was called every imaginable racist slur, felt the sting of being black in a white man's world, and faced inconceivable rejection—even while dressed in my Sunday best in "the house of God" (translation: a church building filled with discriminatory, hateful bigots who shamelessly reserved the right to call people "the N-word" and turn them away at the door). In high school, as much as I wanted to escape it, I was always "that black girl from the islands" whose value wasn't up to par with the rest of the student body. I'll never forget the scoffs, the eye-rolls, the giggles and jeering at my expense… I'll never forget any of it.

Oh, how I *longed for* my home island! There's no describing how often I dreamed of going back to where my heart was happy and my surroundings were stable.

At least I had my baby brother, though. There was always comfort in knowing Phillip and I had a pure, best-buddy friendship that would never be defiled by something as superficial as race or turbulence at home. I always had Phillip to cling to, and him to me, when fighting broke out, things got dangerous, or the environment was shaky.

That is, of course, until he was diagnosed with leukemia at twelve years old and died less than a month later.

Yeah… I definitely had some challenging times in the past.

Oftentimes, folks attempt to comfort another with something similar to the sentiment: "No matter how bad *your* life gets, someone else has it worse." I agree with that notion completely—*I still do!*—and by no means do I believe my circumstances were, or have ever been, more difficult than everyone else. That is simply not my judgment to make (thank God), and engaging in that trail of thought leads to fruitless, petty competitions that only serve to escalate human misery. But I imagine my own story, if shared transparently, might be that very "someone else has it worse" example a number of folks have in mind when they speak those words. The horrors I witnessed *that I would never put in this book* had forged me into something stronger than iron, steel…even titanium. God took my hand in my weakest moments, throughout my grandest despairs, and guided me toward developing this alligator skin I now wore proudly. It was my armor, the thickest and most resilient kind, that no one other than God, Himself, had the power to strip me of. And here I was, brushing my teeth the morning after some devastating news about cancer, knowing in my mind, body, and spirit that God could carry me through *even this.*

I couldn't allow myself to forget that now.

It was then that my decision was made official—signed and sealed; irrevocable. Fearful Lynette got her big sob-fest, and I was sure I would hear from her again, but she *would not* control me. I knew if I continued to feed the wrong inner voice, it would grow like a weed and snuff out whatever potential fruit I had the capacity of bringing forth in God's Name. This cancer in my veins could very well be the platform upon which God could use to reach someone else, and the story could be pitiful or glorious, no matter how long the Almighty planned to keep me here.

I chose glorious.

Faithful Lynette is who I want to be.

I felt the courage swell within me as I rinsed my toothbrush and placed it back in its holder.

No... Faithful Lynette is who I WILL be. I will be strong and do this the right way. Anybody can fall apart under pressure, but it takes a real woman of might *to harness the tenacity God has gifted each of us and face all things through Christ, "who strengthens me," as Philippians 4:13 says. Time to put your big-girl pants on, Lynette.*

My chin lifted a little as my resolve amplified and the adrenaline-induced shaking started to subside.

You are with me, Jesus. None of this is a surprise to you, Lord. You've got me in Your hands, as usual, and I trust You to carry me as You always have.

I lathered some facewash between my palms. And though I was nowhere near a smile, it wasn't "happiness" I was after. It was grit. Determination. Resolve.

You're unstoppable, and You have loaned me Your power from on high, so I, too, am unstoppable.

As my fingers swirled the suds about my forehead, nose, and cheeks, I wasn't any less afraid than I had been, but if my life had taught me one thing I could count on, it was that strength is not found in the *absence* of feelings. Strength is found in carrying out right actions *despite* feelings that would otherwise emotionally paralyze a person into believing they had been crushed or conquered.

Experiencing fear is no doubt a normal part of this diagnosis. Nevertheless, I am Yours, God. I trust You.

After half a minute of scrubbing, I splashed cool water over my face, patted it dry, and watched as the water sunk down into the drain. It was only the surface of my skin that had been given a fresh, clean start, but it meant more than that to me. Bringing my eyes up again to my reflection, I saw a *different* kind of fresh, clean start. If young Mary—who was around the age of fourteen when the angel revealed she would become with child and carry the Savior into the world, forfeiting the normal life she had prior—could say to God, "Be it unto me according to thy word" (Luke 1:28), then so could the woman in the mirror. As children of the King, we are called to be Christ-like. If Jesus—in His most petrified hour, facing an agonizing death for the sake of all mankind—could say to the Father, "Not as *I* will, but as *thou* wilt" (Matthew 26:39), then so could the woman in the mirror.

If Neo could take the red pill and give up blissful ignorance in trade for dystopian horrors in the interest of his fellow man…then so could the woman in the mirror.

I knew very well that this was going to be the roughest, scariest, and most vulnerable ride this life had ever taken me on. I could never carry out this journey alone. Thankfully, for me, I didn't have to.

I'm not alone. You've got me, Father God. I'm scared out of my mind… but I'm willing to fight for Your cause, whether I comprehend the purposes behind its twists and turns or not. I choose the red pill. Let's see just how deep this rabbit hole goes.

Chapter Seven

WESTERN VS. NATURAL —ROUND ONE

With newfound resolve, I navigated the excruciating emotional labyrinth of calling my family members, one after another. The news landed likc a brick through glass each time without deviation. Not one person in my familial circle could have ever seen ovarian cancer coming. Over and over, I was faced with delivering the blow to those who would have sworn my irregularity was nothing more than an age-related issue or fiber deficiency because, as we all agreed, I had always been "so healthy."

I've never been one to beat around the bush. Ripping the Band-Aid off quick and getting straight to the wound would certainly be harsh, but in the long run, I knew it would be better than teasing my loved ones with false hope for thirty minutes just to give them horrible news in the end, anyway, so I got to the point right away each time. My opener, just after the trading of hellos, was: "I'm sorry to tell you this, but you should know that the reason I haven't been feeling well lately is because I have ovarian cancer."

Though I will never forget the heartbreaking stab each phone call brought my heart, I only remember the details of those conversations in flashes.

My baby sister, Mary, fell to the floor, crying inconsolably. A short time later, she was joined by Laura, my elder sister and a registered nurse, who held Mary in her arms as they sobbed together. Phillip, my oldest son from Oregon, was ravaged with grief, dropping everything in his life in the days following to come and see me in person. It was the first of many not-so-casual social calls he would make to be with me as much as possible during appointments and treatments.

My son, Phillip, visiting in September 2021; deep sadness lurks behind these picture-ready smiles

Adam, my son living close by in Los Angeles, followed suit, receiving this update with unimaginable dread and making it a priority to remain by my side as often as he could (and as my condition worsened, his visits increased). Kyle, my mid-twenties son from a neighboring town only a twenty minutes' drive from my house, responded with a fierce anger—not toward me, but toward the helplessness he felt in having no way of rescuing his mother, with whom he felt incredibly close. My grandchildren each reacted in their own tearful way, finding their grandmother's "irreversible" sickness unfathomable to the point that, at times, they could only look at me in silence while tears streamed down their faces and fearful concepts of this mystery-event called "death" entered their thoughts. Isaac and Daniel, my two youngest sons, still lived with me at the time of the news. I took a turn in each of their rooms, sitting down with them and telling them everything, begging them not to cry… A mother forever feels that it is her job to fix whatever hurts her children, and I knew this would bring limitless hurt to them, but this time, I couldn't fix it, so I needed them to be strong for all our sake. In the end, they were champions; they did cry, but silently so, while they sat gathering their composure.

When everyone in the family knew, it was time to start the process all over again with my friends list.

Oftentimes in stories like these, we expect to hear that some relief lies on the other side of having everyone informed. That was not the case for me. I am a solid rock in my family, a true mama to everyone. When pain or heartache threatens the happiness of one of my own, I'm the first on the scene to find a silver lining, a bright side, or a happy thought to ease the pain. Wild horses couldn't stop me from identifying the source of any malady confronting my family and doing whatever I have to do to conquer it...but this time *I was* the source of the malady, and that was at least a thousand times more emotionally exhausting. So much of my own heart had already been tied up in worrying about everyone else's comfort that, when the terrible facts of my condition had officially been conveyed to all, I had nothing left to offer that sick woman in the mirror.

And with each round of delivering blows, another layer of heaviness was added to my growing fortress of dread as I began to wonder just how long I had left. Would my story be like some who receive treatment, hear that glorious word "remission," and go on to live long and prosperous lives afterward? Or would I be among the *unlucky* ones?

One well-meaning family member of mine took it upon himself to research ovarian cancer and corresponding survival rates, and the result was not ideal. The great and powerful information highway known as the Internet can be a wonderful tool in many cases. However, when it comes to researching medical topics, it can be a trainwreck of misinformation and terrifying details. Worst of all, it's a platform upon which numerous voices from the medical world—each one an established professional in their field (and therefore considered an expert on the subject)—can post information and advice that *conflicts with* expert peers within that same field. One doctor with an entire alphabet of impressive credentials following their surname can say, "Whatever you do, *don't* do [this or that]! Your life depends on it!" Another doctor with the same credentials in the very next article will write, "No matter what, make *sure* you do [the same thing the last doctor said to never do]! Your life depends on it!" If even the grandest authorities in the medical world with certifications and degrees out the wazoo can't agree on the essentials of treatment, diet, and critical lifestyle changes that support a longer lifespan for cancer patients, what chance did my family member have of finding solace about *my* situation, or even a reliable answer to how long I could be expected to live? In the end, the answers he landed on were diabolical: I was *not* going to survive this bout with ovarian cancer for very long, his research stated.

This information refreshed all my feelings of despair, renewing within me all fears that I had cried about in the privacy of my bathroom the morning after the conversation with Dr. Bakir. I was still needed here on this earth, and this new bit of data was threatening that all over again, forcing to the forefront of my thoughts every doubt about what my family was going to do without me, all the pain I couldn't be here to alleviate, who would take care of John, my children, the dogs...all of it came flooding back.

As it turned out, many others had the same idea to surf the net and tell me what they had learned. In the days following these phone calls, my cell phone blew up nonstop with ideas, tips, tricks, and advice from friends and family all over who wanted to help in some way. Of course, I get it—that desperation one feels when he or she only wants to rush to a loved one's aid with whatever hope they can offer—and let me state for the record that *I appreciated it with all my heart!* I really and truly did. Without a single, solitary doubt in my mind, I knew, still know, and will always know that this kind of assistance from my beloved companions was offered in my interest and in the most profound gesture of care and concern. And for that reason, I cherish every text, email, and call that came in from these precious souls who wanted to assist me during this terrible time.

However, in the same vein as the Internet with its interminably conflicting expert suggestions and counsel, a lot of my friends and family had no idea that the advice they sent me was diametrically opposed to the advice just sent by someone else. In addition to the occasional shout-out regarding Western treatment options, they referred to all sorts of natural treatment plans that their research claimed would work based on many online testimonials from individuals on platforms and websites like YouTube or TikTok, who believe they had been healed from their cancerous affliction: special thirty-day fasts, a diverse assortment of cannabis-sourced oils, various animal de-worming medications...the list went on and on. Recommendations poured in from everywhere pointing to all sorts of stories online, many of which argued that *they* had the *real* cure, while the rest were pure hokum or scams.

From early on, I was blasted with the "natural vs. Western medicine" conundrum, and as you readers can imagine, each claimed the other would be the death of unsuspecting victims.

Western medical authorities insisted that natural cures were a waste of time and money because they simply couldn't help something as serious as cancer, so a patient could literally die while drinking tea and praying for miracles—"a tragedy that *could have* been avoided if the patient would have only taken their meds like they were told," the articles collectively said. Behind these statements, however, is also the matter of motive or agenda: How many of these men and women were driven by the honest need to help others versus those driven by the almighty, pharmaceutical dollar? (I'm not touching on a mere "conspiracy theory" here, either. There are "bad guys" in every line of work. Though there are certainly countless folks in the medical world who only want to help other people feel better [*and praise the Lord for them!*], there are, absolutely, *some* who will use every scare tactic they can to intimidate patients away from any avenue of help that didn't originate through the same medical system that puts money in their own bank accounts. Many people have stood in white lab coats with their name embroidered on them for commercials, promotions, website banners, etc., making sworn statements about the efficacy of a new drug without a) having been a part of the peer-reviewed research team that developed it; or b) even knowing much about the "exciting, new product" they're agreeing to advocate for. Though I *want to* believe they are all sincere, I know that many human beings give into the influence of sinful greed and endorse whatever they must to increase the jingle of their coin purse. History has proven this to be true, as many, *many* doctors and specialists throughout time have been heavily fined or faced jail time for making false statements about medicine. We, the patients, are left without any way of knowing what "expert advice" is real against that which is inspired by questionable or dubious intentions. And who wants to sort *that* out just after hearing they may be facing the grave?!)

Resistance came from the other side as well: Naturopathic and holistic practitioners frequently explain how plants rich in vitamins are not only more biologically efficient for the human body to ingest, but they are also often the very ingredients Western medicines were built from in labs in the beginning, making them the more obvious choice that promises to give a cancer patient the purest form of healing. Chemotherapy, they explain, does what it says it will in regard to killing cancer cells, but it's all those healthy cells chemo kills off that truly jeopardizes a person. A patient could easily be made far more ill and vulnerable by cooperating with Western treatments—"a tragedy that *could have* been avoided if the patient would have only stayed away from those harsh, Western chemicals," those voices, too, collectively said.

"Do this."

"Don't do that!"

"Take these."

"Don't take those!"

"*This* stuff will kill you!"

"*That* stuff will kill you!"

"Whatever you do…your life depends on [fill-in-the-blank counsel that contradicts the last/next counsel]."

And, on top of all of this overwhelming information overload is the fact that almost every prescription drug has side effects requiring more prescription drugs to counter them, all of which could be dangerously affected by taking something else. So, even if a person in my position was inclined to follow all the natural advice out there, I could end up harming myself (or worse) by taking an unapproved supplement that cancelled out, or clashed with, the cancer treatment my doctors were about to put me on.

What a consuming loop…

As the advice kept rolling in, my head spun until I decided the only thing to do was to tell everyone the *best* "treatment plan" for me was prayer. It was something anyone could carry out on my behalf and, unlike lengthy research into the world of incompatible reports and confusing data, it could be done without any cost to the giver beyond a couple of minutes out of their day. I also figured since the One on the receiving end of those prayers was the Master Physician, it would be a petition directly to my *primary* Primary Doctor to give me the most ideal care. This Doctor—this beautiful, wonderful Cancer Expert who is the very personification of love and care for His people since the beginning of time as documented throughout His Word—would never and could never be motivated by impure desire to put me on the wrong medicines…and *His* advice could be counted on!

One day down the road, I would realize just how much I believed this to be true, when I unplugged from the Matrix for real, took God's "red pill," embraced the journey down *His* "rabbit hole" (a pleasant ride, indeed!), threw my life into the hands of the Great Physician, and abandoned all treatment plans in exchange for His. That would be the day I'd get my life back, despite the prognosis of every human practitioner who had weighed in on my situation…

But before I would ever come to that epiphany, there were lessons to learn along my journey, and at this time, I would have given anything for even a single moment of peace from the ceaseless spinning. I only wanted to stop and take a badly needed breath. Just one. Only for a moment.

The spinning didn't stop. Not then. I couldn't gather my thoughts, and it was clear the harder I tried to force that to happen, the more I heaped frustration and confusion upon myself as every minute of every day brought more and more guidance about what I should or shouldn't do.

Meanwhile, Dr. Bakir's office notified me that I would be hearing from an oncologist within the next few days to take a deeper, far more informed look at exactly what it was we were dealing with. A part of me was already so exhausted with the barrage life had just thrown at me that I didn't want to hear any more about…well, *any of this*, really. The part of me that wore the alligator skin, though—that Faithful Lynette within me who outshined Fearful Lynette that very same morning at the edge of the bathtub—knew I was, in fact, made of a metal strong enough to face this next appointment.

The red pill is very hard to swallow, sometimes. But when the oncologist's office summoned me for my first appointment, I would be there.

Chapter Eight

BIG BLACK BLOBS

Days later, after driving around for thirty minutes along a heavily trafficked freeway, John and I parked in the lot belonging to one of California's most impressive cancer treatment centers, which was several stories tall with multiple attached offices and departments of the same size all stretching over an *enormous* patch of real estate. The sun brought fresh life down to the palm trees situated here and there along the outside of the building's numerous quarters, its rays sparkling off the surface of a few of the facility's nearby pools like glass. Nurses, medical personnel, and patients alike strolled along the outdoor rock walkway encircling the tri-level fountain, sharing laughs, trading conversation, and taking in California's best, brightest weather.

The moment I stepped inside the main entrance, I was taken aback by my surroundings. The scene was spectacular: window panels stretching upwards of twenty-five to thirty feet tall, providing views of the mountains in the distance behind tracts of the bustling city in the foreground; bright green, leafy plants scattered about everywhere, bringing an undertone of health and vitality to the environment; white walls bedecked sporadically with rich, wood-stained acoustic slat-panels illuminated by recessed lighting; waiting rooms in several directions equipped with lavish rugs, couches, and cushioned chairs situated around tempered-glass coffee tables; majestic, Ansel-Adams-like landscape photographs or lifelike, colorful, ripe fruits hung along the walls of the foyer and continuing down the hallways… It was simply striking—not at all the same sterile feel one might have in mind when imagining the layout of a cancer treatment or research building.

What a pretty place. If I didn't know better, I thought to myself, *I would think this was a luxury resort.*

Yet, far from only a warm and fancy hotel feel, the designers had managed to pull off a pricey, sophisticated, scientific quality in the layout as well. Each department's greeting area showcased vast, high-tech computer screens manned by operators sitting confidently in brand-spanking-new swivel chairs, taking calls with jovial tones and clacking away at their well-lit keyboards—and whenever a door swung open off to the side, visitors could catch a peek of the futuristic equipment beyond. If this was the impression patients were given ten feet past the front door, one could only imagine what kind of state-of-the-art machinery and gadgets were whirring away behind some of those handsome walls.

It was obvious to all guests that this facility spared no expense—a natural relief for first-time visitors who needed to know their life-or-death situation would be addressed with the most modern and cutting-edge technologies while their lives were in the hands of the most capable, well-educated specialists that only "a place like this" could afford.

"Wow," I commented to John, "this place is impressive!"

But just as soon as the words were uttered, in a flash, I remembered what was posted on the main sign outside. Despite the momentary comforts from absorbing the stunning atmosphere, references to cancer had become quite personal and distressing of late. I wasn't here for a weekend getaway or to appreciate how efficiently *others* would be treated… I was here, walking upright and painless for the moment, to address the horrors that were just around the corner for *me*.

Twelve centimeters. The size of my ovarian-cancer mass, I reminded myself.

What a strange dichotomy: how quickly a place so extraordinary and remarkable could go from sunny and gorgeous to dark and foreboding. However, something had changed in me that, for better or for worse, had numbed me emotionally, at least for the time being.

In the days leading to this oncology consultation, the size of the mass within me became a subject of macabre curiosity. When someone is initially told they have been diagnosed with cancer, it's the word "cancer," itself, that requires recognition before other details can be processed. Meanwhile, the size and scope of the shadowy forms on a scan are just descriptions of something a person in my position doesn't know how to comprehend anyway, so we loop for a while on the six-letter word-of-death until we've exhausted our shock-response system. Now that I'd had a couple weeks to acknowledge the cause behind it, the words "twelve centimeters" had become...well...less terrifying and more *unbelievable*—like I was the main character in a cartoon or the brunt of some stand-up comedian's joke at a night-club session. Using the limited knowledge I had of medical references and methods of measurement, I wrapped the concept into terms I could understand: To birth a baby, a mother has to be dilated to ten centimeters, and that is considered large—yet, here I was, carrying a bulk of death-tissue larger than *that*.

A cartoon. That's what I was now.

Don't misunderstand. This *was* real; by the time of this appointment, I had accepted that. However, a person can only take so much before their shock meter is fatigued and they're left standing, blinking, blank-faced and sensationless. The emotional rollercoaster has lows, like the big bathtub cry, and it has highs, like the alligator skin I can be proud of, but once in a while, you just coast straight. Somewhere within me, where the fear about this mass should have been, was a void, a nothingness, a complete hollow vacuum where all feelings go to die. Perhaps it was another symptom of shock? Maybe God, Himself, instilled a mysterious superpower within human subconsciousness that made us all capable of shutting off the emotional valve so we can take in the onslaught of horror and do what we need to survive? All I knew was, the more I tried to force all these details about cancer and masses into my cognitive mind, the more I was beginning to become numb on the inside about the whole ordeal. I would *never* lose that anxious edge when thoughts of leaving my family hit me, but ironically, the particulars related to the cancer—the huge mass that was the very reason my family's stability was threatened in the first place—were received without much panic as the days passed.

Thankfully for me, that's right where I needed to be for this appointment, because what I was about to see was inconceivable.

Shortly after I reported to the receptionist, I was led down a few grand hallways past many immaculately clean rooms to the ovarian cancer office. Fun, childlike paintings of giraffes, butterflies, and other creatures of wildlife were hanging in frames around this doctor's certificates and accolades. I looked around, believing it would be the first of many visits in this room and I may as well get used to it and make myself at home.

Little did I know in that moment—though I was about to find out—I would not be seeing this doctor again after that day, and for good reason.

The mid-forties, female Caucasian specialist entered in her white foam clogs, blue pants, and lab coat with her assistant following closely behind her. Her voice was soothing as she greeted me and removed her COVID mask so I could see her sincerely smiling face while we exchanged social-distanced greetings from around six feet away.

"Nice to meet you, too," I said in cooperation with formality. Secretly, I was hoping she would just get to the point. Graciously, she did just that. Before she ever addressed my circumstances, she knew this would be our one and only meeting.

Without missing a beat, the doctor displayed my MRI scans on her computer monitor, adjusting the screen toward John and me. For the first time, I was able to see with my very own eyes what damage the silent assassin named Cancer had done to me thus far, but I couldn't begin to interpret what my eyes were taking in. Every place we looked, it was darkened with disease—just blackness everywhere. I had no idea what body part I was looking at as my eyes skipped around the scans: The overwhelming dark, dark…*dark* all over the place visually communicated nothing more to me personally than a big, black, blurry blob unlike any X-ray, chart, or human body illustration I had ever seen, even in school textbooks during health class.

"If you look here," the doctor pointed to one of many murky blotches, "you will see that the cancer has spread to the lungs and stomach."

Those were my lungs and stomach? Wait a second. Where did my lungs end and my stomach begin? How could she—how could *anyone*—even tell? She could have easily glued a piece of black construction paper to the front of her computer screen for the rest of her morbid presentation and I would have been none the wiser.

"And here, and here," she redirected, "we see cancer in the breasts and ovaries."

You mean that black blob? Or the other black blob? I tried to follow along in silence, knowing my questions were so rudimentary that I could drastically delay the appointment's timely progress by forcing this woman to start at the beginning, so I just blinked and stared as she continued poking her finger about the indistinct, cloudy shapes.

"Over here we have evidence that it's in the bones as well, so, this shows us the cancer has metastasized throughout."

Numbness… Lack of feeling… "Metastasized" was beginning to affect me in a similar way as the words "twelve centimeters." The language had lost all meaning. It simply wouldn't compute. The world was spinning, and there was no indication it would ever stop, so I resigned myself to standing in the middle of the twister, numb and stupefied. The doctor was pointing, naming body parts, and talking about her observations of the data, but even cold pancake syrup would have moved too fast for me in that moment, as dazed and dumbfounded as I was by the incoming details. I was "listening," attempting to receive her words as quickly as they fell from her mouth, but the sight of the lion's share of my own body tissues heavily riddled with colossal, shadowy infection extending from one extreme edge of the scans to the other was just adding intense, white-noise static to my already fragmented comprehension.

What was wrong with me? Wouldn't anyone else in my shoes be trembling? Wasn't this supposed to be scary? Wasn't I supposed to be bursting into tears while nurses surrounded me with boxes of tissues and reassuring pats on the shoulder? Isn't that how this was supposed to go down? Why was I just sitting here, withdrawn into a catatonic or comatose state of nonbeing? Why was I so dead inside to this grand blast of medical terminology and jargon describing masses and blobs?

And uh…what was that look she just gave me? Did I detect a slight look of puzzlement on her face?

Something wasn't right. It was okay if *I* was confused, and I was fine with it if John was as well, but the *doctor* shouldn't be.

I locked my eyes on hers as she swiveled the screen back to face her and her assistant and furrowed her brow.

"The thing is, ovarian cancer doesn't behave like this," she said.

Hope sprung up to my throat, clinging to her doubt as if it were a promise of longevity over my life.

Maybe this whole thing was a mistake. Maybe everyone up to this point had been wrong. Could it be that I didn't have cancer after all, and these scans were showing some cancer-copycat condition that would free me from the bonds of death? Some benign, albeit scary looking, Behemoth-cyst pustule-thing that could be treated with a week of antibiotics?

Unfortunately, my optimism died as quickly as it had come.

Clasping her hands together with a quiet slap, she turned to me directly, abandoning the blobs.

"It's breast cancer."

Blink. Stare.

Numb.

"It started at the breasts and metastasized down to the ovaries," she further explained when I didn't respond. "That would certainly account for the presence of the mass, as well as any bowel discomfort you may have been experiencing. So, I'm going to schedule you with a breast cancer oncologist. They will take a look at these images and make a determination about your treatment."

Well, that explains her puzzled expression, I ruminated. *She's clearly confused as to why I was ever brought to her when I should have gone to a different specialist.*

Thank God I was emotionally comatose now. I wonder what I would have done if I could have actually felt the sting of yet another delay, another specialist, another appointment, another mystery, another analysis of how and when I would meet my Maker.

Back in the car, John and I rode in silence. Just like the night Dr. Bakir called to inform me that I was being chased by the six-letter assassin, an unspoken agreement had been officiated between me and my husband: There was literally nothing to say, for in those moments when words fail to bring solace to a fresh wound, any sound uttered is simply noise to a broken spirit.

Chapter Nine

HURRY UP AND WAIT

All my prayer-warrior friends had received a call from me between the appointment with the ovarian cancer oncologist and the subsequent appointment with the breast cancer oncologist. I wasn't myself anymore, and though I didn't want to usher in another wave of conflicting advice from my friends' Internet surfing, I *did* need prayer, so my trusted inner circle was informed that I had been misdiagnosed and it was actually *breast* cancer we were facing (though, technically, that had yet to be officially confirmed).

The emotional roller coaster that had become the definition of my life was still up, down, and sideways: Some days I was a rock star, looking cancer in the face and simply *daring* it to threaten a child of God. It was during those times I felt like Joan of Arc just before she led her French troops into the siege of Orléans—my metaphorical sword held high, charging into battle with shouts of victory well before my blade made its first clang against Cancer's pathetic poking stick: Huzzah! Other days, I had to muster every ounce of strength I had just to face another hour without giving into deep depression over the demoralizing fact that I *still* didn't have any answers, and the only guesses I could muster on my own were related to a demoralizing prognosis. On those occasions, I felt like a walking abstract Picasso painting: lopsided, distorted, and disproportionate body parts all messed up and painted on where they shouldn't be—a disturbing fusion of black blobs melting together on a canvas of MRI scans; defeated already by the mighty champion, Cancer, who had probably killed me already through only the power of a casual scoff. And, of course, there were days that slipped by when I felt almost nothing, just as I had when I viewed those scan-blobs—disassociated from reality, floating above life and watching, disconnected, detached…*numb.*

As often as possible, I would try to keep my hands busy doing something productive. Countless times, between minor chores or phone calls for prayer, I felt tempted to bite my nails again like I used to. Thankfully, I managed to avoid giving in to that old habit, but it was challenging, spending so many hours grounded at home, unable to work. "Stir crazy" is a deficient term for my situation; I was "stir-*insane*," sitting, waiting, wasting away, and feeling just the beginning phases of weakness creeping into my physical body.

I didn't blame the Western system for messing up my diagnosis. That really could have happened with anyone. It wasn't like it caused a really long delay.

I was relieved when the next appointment came quickly.

In less than a week, I was back at the "luxury hotel" cancer center with John, being led down a different hallway to the breast cancer portion of the facility. From this secondary waiting room, just following the documentation of my vitals with a medical assistant, the doctor with whom I would spend most of my treatment time came to retrieve me personally.

"Lynette Hill?" she called from the doorway. "I'm Dr. Ibrahim."

I recall my first impression of her when she called me back. Her impeccable taste in clothing—black pants, black turtleneck, and shiny gold belt around the waist—was a nice departure from the scrubs I had grown accustomed to. Though she had a lab coat on, it was left hanging open in the front to exhibit her fashionable, youthful style. She was masked for COVID protocol, as we all were, but her Syrian accent made her covered face more exotic, like one of those mysterious, Middle Eastern women in robes who hide all but their eyes behind a veil. That was how striking her eyes were when we met: beautiful, warm, and friendly, reassuring her patients with a mere glance that she was alert and deeply aware of their needs.

I'm grateful that this was not merely a first impression, but a commercial for how she would continue to interact with me in the days to come. When the blobs were back up on the monitor minutes later, her light, happy tones cast a layer of sugar over the bitter visuals, making them just a touch easier to swallow.

"I agree with the ovarian specialist," her cheerful voice dipped slightly. "We *are* looking at breast cancer here."

One major question answered at last! I celebrated prematurely. *Maybe we're getting somewhere? Can we finally begin treatment now?*

"In order to confirm this diagnosis officially, we're going to need to run a test—"

Ugh. So close…

"—to determine where the cancer originated from for certain. We'll need to gather some tissue from the breast and abdomen. As soon as those results come back to confirm my suspicions, we will be able to move forward with treatment."

Suddenly, John piped in, asking the "elephant in the room" question that nobody up to this point would answer, despite that it had been asked a few times.

"How long before Lynette… How much time does she have left?"

Dr. Ibrahim shifted on her small, round swivel stool. She regarded us empathetically as she hesitated for only a moment, but in that tiny amount of time, she conveyed a lifetime of compassion. This was a woman who dealt with sick people every hour of every day. Delivering horrible news and watching disease steal life from her patients was as routine for her as an auto mechanic popping the hood of a car…and she didn't know *me* at all. We didn't have an established friendship or even the beginning of a conventional, doctor-patient relationship at this point. She could have easily acted as if John's question was predictable, mundane, or inconvenient—answering with aloof and impersonal indifference toward us to fulfill only what was necessary within the requirements of a job description. And though that kind of cavalier response from a doctor would have been hurtful, it wouldn't have been a surprise. Yet, in this single, silent gaze, her eyes told me she wasn't regarding me as merely the next in line to receive her services. She felt the weight of our horror, and it showed. Her heart was breaking for us. She cared for me as an individual human being, of equal value to her, with feelings, a concerned family, a lifetime of established relationships, and a whole world of my own that had just screeched to a stop.

She *cared.*

And it may have been because she cared that she responded the way she did, though alas, it would not result in an answer to John's delicate question.

"We're not going to talk about length of remaining life at this point. We're going to see what we're dealing with first and talk about treatment. The scans… Well, the scans don't look good," she turned her eyes to me, "but we're going to focus on giving you excellent quality of life for as long as you're here."

"Quality of life"…

I knew what *that* meant.

In itself, it was still an answer, even if an indirect one. Though it was delivered with supreme tenderness, it was that "palliative care" response one gets from a medical professional when death is a certainty and approaching fast. It's the same line the movies and television shows drop when preparing someone for the worst, when there's no avoiding eventual death—and often in agonizing ways—but the care team intends to "make the patient as comfortable and pain-free as possible" before the end. By choosing not to answer the question and referring to my "quality of life," Dr. Ibrahim had effectively dealt the blow John and I feared most. I *was* dying, and by now I was past the point of no return, even if this sweet, Syrian medical maven couldn't bring herself to say it outright… and it was happening fast. If my symptoms thus far were any indication of how quickly the cancer was spreading within me—from "I can't use the restroom" to "quality of life" in a matter of mere weeks—then where would I be in another week or two?

It didn't look good.

And what was I expecting, anyway? Had there been, perhaps buried somewhere deep, some hope that she would look at us like we were nuts, lean forward, and say, "Lynette, we're not talking about *death*, here; we're talking about *recovery*," followed by a confident, celebratory smile and a round of "Kumbaya"?

Maybe, yeah. As unrealistic as that would have been, I guess if I'm honest, I was pleading with God and the universe that she would dispel all my fears and give me good news. After all, up to this appointment, each time I asked about what was truly wrong with me or what my future looked like, I was instructed to wait for the *next* doctor or specialist to speak to those issues since they would be the one whose field of expertise and education qualified them to predict such matters. The tiny glimmer of hope that kept me facing one day after another throughout this nightmare was clinging to the (false) promise that I would finally arrive to a meeting with *the* specialist and hear that everyone before her was jumping to the wrong conclusions; that I was "fine," as I told myself a thousand times in the beginning; that I *could* "remain calm" because something was missed in the scans that proved this condition was reversible with some medication or therapy...

Yet, here she was, *the* specialist of specialists whose training qualified her to confirm or deny my future on this earth, and instead of Kumbaya and hugs, I was given the "quality of life" line.

Additionally, though my worst fear about death had been confirmed, one particularly nagging inquiry—*how long I had left to live*—was left up in the air. Why wouldn't anyone answer that? Didn't I, the person whose lifespan was being debated, have a right to know how many days, weeks, or months I would continue to inhabit this physical body?

What are you thinking in that pretty head of yours? I pondered as I looked into Dr. Ibrahim's bright brown eyes. *Why won't you tell me what I want to know? Why won't you answer John's question?*

She met my gaze, and I observed a mysterious hesitation—something undefinable within her that kept her from saying anymore on the subject. Though the part of me that had been exhausted beyond all measure with weeks of vague responses from preliminary medical personnel wanted to explode with demands—stand to my feet, hands on my hips, finger wagging, voice raised—I made the inconceivable decision to trust Dr. Ibrahim in that moment. The way she was looking at me... She really did care. Therefore, I would receive that gift of genuine concern and respond with trust in her reasoning behind avoiding a straight answer for the time being. As frustrating as it was that we still had no clue how long I would be here, I reminded myself she wasn't the enemy. *Cancer* was the enemy, and Dr. Ibrahim was on my side in the battle against it.

An opportunity was given for John and me to ask any additional questions we may have had, but what on earth would we ask? As I had always been healthy and had never been in close proximity to a cancer situation, I didn't know enough about the subject to have formed an arsenal of questions to shoot out in the first place. At this point, thanking the kind lady for her time and care, and proceeding to *get the heck outta Dodge*, was the true next step in my treatment, as far as I was concerned.

It would be weeks before the biopsies Dr. Ibrahim ordered were carried out. There is no describing how taxing and tedious a "sit and do nothing" period can be on a person whose life hangs in the balance. Only those who have lived my story can even begin to speak to how laborious this brand of "downtime" is between diagnosis and treatment.

On the one hand, a person has essentially been told they could die a horrible death if they don't act quickly and do what they've been instructed to do; on the other hand, there is nothing *to* do except show up to one appointment after another and then "hurry up and...wait" during the interim. Taking calls, twiddling thumbs, reading the Bible, praying, singing the occasional hymn, desperately trying to remain faithful, and sitting on one's hands to avoid returning to an old nail-biting habit is a person's sole activity roster. Everything else in that person's life has been placed on a grueling pause: A challenged immunity system meant I couldn't go out and about in public like I used to lest I be exposed to something egregious—and as far as we knew, at that time, COVID was spreading like a brushfire that couldn't be mitigated regardless of global quarantines; the vitality I used to feel was draining from me as my body was utilizing every minutia of strength to fight a losing battle, so even odd jobs around my house and property were starting to become too much to take on; wrestling with the dogs in the yard was an activity requiring not only energy but interest, and with all this talk of cancer and death, tussling and sweating with the dogs in the hot California sun was quickly becoming a pastime; obviously I couldn't work, and church or school functions were out of the question.

Everything—*everything in my entire life*—was halted while I waited.

And waited.

...And waaaited...

Some days passed faster than others, and those were the days that kept me sane. Loved ones called often to pray with me and trade "I love yous" along with statements of faith, and that, alongside the mindless entertainment provided by the television, managed to help occupy my mind.

Other days slowed to a ruthless crawl—so boring and so monotonous that staring at the wall and counting to a million could have been considered an upgrade to good times.

Meanwhile, I heard a good number of horror stories about just how painful the biopsies were going to be, and that gave me yet another thing to worry about while I lingered at home anticipating a follow-up call from the hospital. Fortunately for me—and I mean that—all the warnings were wrong. Whether it was because my situation was unique, or because the technology behind retrieving biopsy tissue has advanced in recent years, I can't be sure, but it was a fairly simple and painless process to get through.

For the breast biopsy, less than an hour transpired between arrival and departure; they numbed the local area, extracted what they required with a needle, and sent me on my way. Easy-peasy.

The abdominal biopsy was slightly more complicated, but still nothing compared to what I had been told to expect: I was required to arrive at the hospital at eight o'clock in the morning. Following check-in, I was placed in a gown and made to lay on one of seven beds that were separated by privacy curtains while the nurse took vitals and chatted about something menial to help me pass the time until the extraction team one floor below me was ready. Then I was wheeled down several hallways, through a large elevator, and further down to a *freezing* room that smelled of bleach, wherein the pathologist described the process: I would be intravenously sedated, inserted into a machine that would locate the precise location of the mass, suitable tissue would be drawn, and then I would be returned to the first room where my husband would be called to pick me up. From there, the results would be sent to Dr. Ibrahim who would reach out to me with further information in no time. The pathologist spoke about it as if it were a Sunday afternoon picnic or a game of musical chairs, upbeat and positive. However, my life lately had been so hard, so harsh, and so unrelenting that, as much as I appreciated his cheerfulness (like iced tea in a desert—it was *that* refreshing), I couldn't exactly join him in his upbeat mood beyond polite introductions.

Everything went down just as the pathologist described without an issue and, after a nurse found a vein and told me to count to ten (I made it to three), the next thing I remember is waking up to Mr. Merry Disposition telling me the procedure was already over and all had gone well.

Though I was (and still am) happy that the biopsies were a painless success, one particular detail haunts me a little whenever I think back to that day. Due to COVID regulations, John had not been allowed to accompany me into the hospital, and the look on his face when the orderly wheeled me out to the car was tragic. Everything had been smooth, that much he was no doubt grateful for, but John felt his proper place as my husband was *by my side*—not sitting out in a parking lot praying while his wife was out of sight being put to sleep and prodded with sharp needles.

If he only knew then what we know now...

This wouldn't be the only time John and I were separated. The next time that was forced upon us—which happened to be during the following Thanksgiving (explained in the pages ahead)—it would be the most chilling weeks of both our lives, bar none. Prior to that, though, there were several more seasons I was expected to hurry up and wait, beginning with the results of the biopsies.

I don't have the foggiest idea how long pathology normally takes to process in the medical world, but in my case, it was *two additional weeks* of waiting for results following the two weeks I had already waited to have them extracted. Dr. Ibrahim met with me briefly to confirm her initial suspicions: The biopsies showed it *was* breast cancer that had metastasized to ovaries, lungs, stomach, bones—generally, all throughout my body—and it was spreading *fast*. And then she dropped another doozy of a medical term: "stage four."

That's what she said. I had "stage four" breast cancer. And in case you readers don't know what that means, it's the worst and final "stage" cancer can be in. In simple words: "Stage one" refers to cancer that effects a smaller area and is contained within its original organ; "stage two" means the cancer is affecting a larger area, but still contained, though it sometimes refers to the process by which the cells have moved into lymph nodes (a detail that depends on the type of cancer being discussed); "stage three" indicates that the cancer has begun spreading into surrounding tissues but not another organ; "stage four," the scary stage, recognizes that the cancer has spread from its place of origin into another organ...or, in my case, *several* other organs.

Sure, I had heard those words on television or something, and I had even been told in my last visit with Dr. Ibrahim that my cancer had "metastasized," but with all this new language being introduced into my life during the grandest revolving shock-barrage I would ever live through, I didn't clearly understand what it had meant until this point...and it wasn't good news. Whatever my treatment was going to be, we needed to get on with it!

"Stage four," they say, is incurable: yet another confirmation that I wasn't going to make it. But for whatever time I did have left—and all of us agreed I should prolong my life as long as I could—instantaneous action was needed!

Dr. Ibrahim was of the same mind, making it infinitely clear that we needed to start *aggressive* chemotherapy right away. Similar to the urgent care doctor's warning when he called about the "abnormal blood," she also stated: I could *not* wait a month. This was not one of those times I could allow weeks to go by while I took fiber powders and carried on day-to-day activities with plans to eventually take care of myself while I blew off appointments. I had to get started on these medications absolutely right that second! I needed to hurry up and—!!

...wait some more weeks. Even with my life hanging in the balance, dangling by a splitting, tearing thread while due process dragged its feet, treatment could not begin without approval from my medical insurance company.

In cases like these, insurance companies won't take very seriously a phone call from the patient directly. It's not like they're being asked to send a hundred bucks to reimburse a patient for getting a boo-boo-scrape on a knee from falling in a pair of skates with the neighborhood kids. They are looking at having to shell out major dollar amounts in coverage for a cancer patient, so they won't budge until they hear from the doctor, personally (and, evidently, repeatedly). Since Dr. Ibrahim and her staff were making calls on my behalf to get insurance moving, I was stuck in miserable limbo-land, day after day, simply waiting for the phone to ring and move the proverbial ball toward progress. Sweet Dr. Ibrahim maintained close contact with me during those taxing hours, but all *she* could do was ride the insurance folks and pray right alongside me that someone would get their butt in gear and make something happen. Each time she "updated me" (with no new information, bless her heart), I could sense the pity and/or desperation on her end as well, while the insurance reps asked for more data, more medical history, more records, more copies of the scans, more details leading up to diagnosis, more notes regarding the severity of diagnosis...just a *train load* of preauthorization paperwork, phone calls, emails, and file transfers that was apparently never going to end before they could make the decision to cover my treatment.

At one point, Dr. Ibrahim must have decided she, too, had waited long enough. I don't know exactly what she said and how candidly she said it, but from what I eventually heard later on, she had her own way of letting my insurance company know I could literally die while they were sitting on my case emailing and faxing each other papers. She made it clear she had to begin my treatment *now*, not later. And though I will always be eternally grateful for everything she and her staff did on my behalf, it wasn't until many calls were placed (one of which I understand may have been slightly threatening) that my coverage was approved.

Meanwhile, it was a weeks-long smorgasbord of rigamarole and fussing that *could* have been the difference in whether I lived or died—a fact that didn't escape me for a second as I played the excruciating waiting game. I remember vividly the thoughts plaguing me during that time. More than anything else, I found myself questioning, like a skipping record, how this had become my life. I wanted to scream myself awake from this living nightmare! There I was, at the mercy of an insurance company that didn't know me from Adam and Eve—didn't know the first thing about how I lived, what I believed in, what I stood for, what value I had in my community and family, what I cared about, what I still had to live for, whether I was even ready to face the afterlife; they didn't know *anything*—yet, somehow, my very life hung in the balance of scales *they* controlled.

What a head game…

Around this time, my sister, Laura, had been filled in on the biopsies, learned the corrected cancer diagnosis, and heard about Dr. Ibrahim's reserved response to John's question. Everyone who has been through something similar to my story knows quite well what it feels like to be reminded to "get your affairs in order," but how can a person effectively do so if they don't know how long they have to carry out such an expectation? This bothered Laura, too, who had been following the narrative: We had been told we wouldn't know that answer until we knew exactly where and how far the cancer had spread; then when we did know where the cancer had spread, we were told we wouldn't have a guess about my time left on earth until we knew what kind of cancer we were dealing with; once we knew what kind of cancer I had, we were told we couldn't talk about the length of my life until the point of origin was confirmed through biopsies; and when the biopsies came back, we were told we had to wait until treatment began, *weeks later*, when the insurance kicked into gear... And all the while, I didn't have a guarantee of a "tomorrow," let alone a guarantee of "next month" or however long a person needs to prepare for an event as permanent as their own death. It was starting to look like I was on track to die before anyone could tell me *when* I was going to die—a position that Laura was simply done hearing about.

From the beginning, I had Laura listed as both an emergency contact as well as a family member who was to be given full access to my medical records, past and ongoing. One of Laura's friends in the medical field was an oncologist who was both knowledgeable and discreet enough to be trusted to take a closer look at my scans and answer the otherwise unanswerable question for all our benefit.

But perhaps the word "benefit" is a misnomer in this context...

I was at home in my bedroom, sitting calmly on the bed when the call from Laura came in. She hadn't told me to sit down, but thank God (literally) that I was already sitting on the edge of my bed. Had I been standing, my legs would have caved out from under me. Laura gave it to me straight, though it nearly killed her to do so.

"It's only a matter of months," Laura's friend had said. "Based on how aggressive and far-reaching your sister's cancer is, I'm sorry to say it, but I believe 'months' is what we're looking at here. Make sure you keep your sister comfortable and as pain-free as possible, because she is *not* going to be around much longer now."

It may not have been from my personal oncologist, but it *was* from a professional in oncology with the experience needed to make an educated guess regarding this situation, so her opinion—no, her *conclusion*—was significant and powerful. At long last, after repeated petitions to receive this information, we got it.

...And once we got it, it crossed my mind how cracked-in-the-head it was that we ever wanted it in the first place. It was official: I had only "months" to live. The phrase "a bitter pill to swallow" doesn't even touch the magnitude of the impact this update launched against us all—Laura included, as the news simply broke her.

The cushion of the mattress beneath me curled up around the edges of my thighs, holding me steadfast. As weak as I was from both the cancer and the emotional shock, it was serendipitous I was protected from falling.

Oh God. I'm dying. In only a few months from right this moment, I'll be gone.

I'll...

Be...

Gone...

In "months."

The whirlwind hit me all over again. I gasped for air. Though survival instinct had served me well by numbing my nerves amid the ceaseless volley of horrors in many recent days leading to the delivery of this news, that same instinct was now as silent as the grave that fate was preparing for me. Somewhere in an invisible, alternative reality, my enemy, Cancer, was high-fiving the grim reaper as they jointly dug one menacing shovel-full of dirt from the ground after another. I didn't have to listen hard to hear their revelry, their jeering, their triumphant jests about how silly I had been to think I had a future to look forward to.

Fearful Lynette was feasting.

I told you it was bad. You wouldn't listen, she taunted. *You were so convinced there was hope—that even if you went to be with God before you expected to, you would still have time to prepare everyone, "get your affairs in order," enjoy more family gatherings and happy events. You imagined at least a few more Christmases by the fire, grandkids tearing through pretty paper, or birthday parties with kazoos and festive, pointy hats, even if all of that had to be experienced while you sat in a rocker, rapidly growing old and weak under a lap-quilt while your hair fell strand-by-strand to the floor. You thought the world was your oyster and the journey toward finding the pearl was a lengthy one. See how silly that was? I tried to tell you...*

As the pessimistic one within rambled on, the room spun, circled, whipped around me, objects blurring together in streaks as my thoughts exploded in multiple directions all at once.

Faithful Lynette didn't stand a chance.

Though I had asked myself all fathomable questions that day at the edge of the bathtub, they all came swarming back, demanding with increased exigency that they be acknowledged and addressed: Was this *really* how and when I was going to leave this world? Had I indeed gone through all of my past battles—alligator skin and all—just to end up here, ascending into my eternity while there was so much I still needed to tend to? Would I be strong enough to face the treatment? Would the treatment even be *worth it* if I was on my way out anyway? What about my family?

What about…what about…what about…

It all came crashing back. The barrage, the swarm of chaos, the static, the noise—everything I had conquered that day when Faithful Lynette won the volume competition and renewed my trust in God—returned with a vengeance. The room was getting darker and darker by the second.

I tried what had worked before.

Breathe, Lynette. Just breathe…

But I couldn't breathe. I felt like an elephant was sitting on my chest, squeezing the air from my lungs, oblivious to my plight. Maybe in that same realm where Cancer and Reaper were digging, one might be able to catch a glimpse of the emerald anaconda boa constrictor that was curling around my ribcage, identifying my cancerous flesh as its next meal as soon as I succumbed to the lack of oxygen and allowed it to swallow me whole.

Breathe! my inner voice screamed. *If you don't slow down and take in at least some air, "months" will be off the table, too!*

In…

Out…

Alligator skin.

In…

Out…

Strongest metal; that's what I'm made of.

In…

Out…

Child of God. He has a plan. He must!

None of my go-to self-help refrains were getting through. At last, I had been overpowered.

What I wouldn't have given in that moment for the numbness, the lack of all feeling in the face of mortal disaster, to come back. As great as the internal turmoil was, however, I didn't cry. There would be no purging the poisons through the expulsion of tears. Not this time. And that may have been a blessing in disguise for when John walked in.

In those days, John never stayed away from the house for long. He was quite personally aware of my need for him to remain by my side. At this early point, it was still primarily for emotional and moral support (though neither of us knew just how physical my reliance upon him was about to get). As he sat down next to me, I considered how I was going to deliver the latest punch to his world, but as there was no manual on how to handle these situations and his eyes implored mine for answers I didn't know how else to provide, I opened my mouth and let the frank, cold, harsh words surge.

Immediately afterward, he put his hand on my knee and we sat there, silent.

Once again, for the millionth time in a couple short months, there was nothing to say, there was nothing to do, there was nothing to anticipate or look forward to...

...Except "months," whatever that meant for us.

Chapter Ten

HEAVENLY PERSPECTIVE

"This pill I'm putting you on," Dr. Ibrahim said, "is an oral form of chemotherapy. Unlike the infusions you hear about with other cancer patients, you will just take two daily as directed, but I believe they will be just as aggressive in treating the cancer."

I nodded, trying to make more room in my inundated brain for treatment instructions.

Treatment was *finally* beginning, and despite how long I had waited for that to happen, Laura's friend's words about the "months" I had left were bouncing around my head as loud as Dr. Ibrahim's words about pills. I couldn't help but wonder, if I really did only have a short time left, whether chemotherapy (aggressive or otherwise) would even matter much anyway.

Yet, her following statement did grab my attention.

"Lynette, you need to prepare yourself. This next season in your life is going to be *brutal*."

"Brutal." *That* word landed. I tucked the warning away in my brain's filing system.

"But, if you can get through the hard part—and it *will be hard*," she said earnestly, "we can start focusing on your quality of life. Just power through the beginning, and it *will* get easier."

I was soon about to learn what "hard" truly meant…and neither "hard" nor "brutal" would ever be strong enough for what was coming.

Once the dust settled from my near-hyperventilation-breakdown at the bedside the day Laura called me, I began to consider all the "unanswerables" again from a different angle. As much as possible, before my death in a couple months, I needed to shed my "human perspective" and try on a "heavenly perspective," like the heroes of the New Testament.

And if I was going to be as useful to God and His purpose for me as possible, I needed to snap into this state of mind sooner rather than later, as time was ticking. Of course, that would be a challenge…

The Bible has several verses that initially come across bizarre and hard to comprehend in today's modern world. For the early Christians, that "heavenly perspective" was closer to home. Dying and going to heaven was, for them, a graduation of sorts from the worry and anxiety of this flawed, human condition into the bliss of perfection and divine love for all eternity on the other side. Somehow, we, as a modern society, have lost that understanding along the way, and the heavily sought-after perspective of the apostles and biblical saints regarding the tragedy of death is so much harder to grasp now. We say words out of habit or obligation, like acknowledging that someone has "gone to a better place," but when it comes to genuinely applying that in the face of death, we are *so far removed* from how the ancients felt about these concepts that "heavenly perspective" is traded for an earthly one where we beg God for more time *here*…and then blame Him if we don't get it. Translation: We beg God for more time in this inferior, temporary, fleeting life of hardship and pain, and blame Him for being unfair if He instead chooses to graduate His child to paradise before the rest of us are ready. It's like a young girl crying in despair when she has been told by her mother to come inside and stop playing in the mud; it's her *favorite* recreational activity, so she is distraught and disappointed by her playtime being cut short…but she has no idea that she's been called in to clean up and pack for a trip to Disney World—the "better place." She agonizes for a moment, and her friends from next door also cry at her disappearance, believing the mother to be unfair, but when they're all enlightened enough to fully comprehend the whole story when she returns from her vacation later on, they will all rejoice that she was whisked away from the mud pit and into the Magic Kingdom. They will want to know all about the sights and sounds of her trip, listening enviously to what the young girl was experiencing in a child's paradise while the rest of them had *only* mud to play with. The mother, on the other hand, knew through her unique, parental perspective that *once all the children had complete understanding*, they would no longer mourn over the day the mud-play ended before they were ready.

How often we cry over the loss of this transitory place so filled with pain, failing to completely and maturely comprehend that those who have accepted Christ as their Savior will be taken into a place of ceaseless, eternal joy and glory! All the while, God knows through His unique, omniscient perspective that *once all His children have complete understanding*, we will no longer mourn over the day a loved one left the "mud-pit" of earthly life and playtime before we were ready.

Until then, the loss of life is seen as tragic: an "earthly perspective."

That might be why it's difficult for contemporary believers to wrap their brains around verses that say we should *rejoice in* pain, suffering, and death. Nevertheless, that language is peppered all throughout the Word of God by writers such as Peter, James, Paul, and others: Peter wrote that we should expect hardships when we walk with Christ and anticipate feeling overjoyed when God's glory is revealed *within* that hardship (1 Peter 4:12–13); James, the half-brother of Christ, alongside Paul, both wrote that we should consider all trials and tribulations of this earthly experience pure *joy*, because that testing of our faith increases our perseverance, rendering a more mature, faithful servant of God (James 1:2–4; Romans 5:3–5); Paul, to the church in Corinth, wrote that we should delight in life's difficulties for Christ's sake, because through those experiences our real strength reveals itself (2 Corinthians 12:10); to the Philippians, Paul wrote that we should participate in the suffering of Christ, because doing so makes us *more like Him* (Philippians 3:10); and unbelievably, Paul, to the church in Philippi, went as far as to write that death is a "gain" for us believers, as it unites us with Christ, which, as he put it, is the "far better" position to be in (Philippians 1:21, 23)!

"To die is *gain*"…? Now *that* is an excellent example of the "heavenly perspective" if there ever was one. And it was this concept that—like a seed planted in my youth and watered during seasons of growth in my faith since—was starting to take root and sprout in my heart and mind while the words "months to live" made their impact. Regardless of the circumstances behind when and how I passed into eternity, death would not be the end for me; *it would be the beginning*. And since my death was (evidently) inevitable and approaching fast, there was no time like the present to accept that transition for what it really was and show the world around me the greatest example of Christ-like attitude and behavior up to my final breath!

However, there is a very, *very* important balance here that kept me from just leaping into "Lord take me home" mode…and that, too, was a biblical concept. The apostles weren't just a bunch of crazy guys who loved suffering and couldn't wait to die; remembering them in that inaccurate light would be a disastrous misinterpretation of Scripture. Paul *also* made it clear—and in the same passage, I might add—that there is "fruitful" work we are expected to do while we're here (Philippians 1:22).

So, was it my time to let go and be united with Christ? Or was it my time to stay and be fruitful here?

When the rubber met the road, I never gave up believing that God had a plan for me. However, as all signs were pointing to that plan coming to an abrupt end in mere weeks, I felt I had to be all the more faithful in my willingness to walk it out; whatever impact I could make in the days leading to my own ascension to heaven had to be identified and applied *now*, as "later" wasn't an option. Some biblical characters had accomplished their magnum-opus purpose with years to spare, while others accomplished their supreme calling *through the reality of death*. Christ, Himself, would forever be the ultimate example of such a feat. Had He lived many years beyond that petrifying night in Gethsemane, He wouldn't have fulfilled His perfect role as the Passover Lamb sent to die "the criminal's death" in order to beautifully and ironically pave the way for the worst of criminals to enter the presence of the Father in eternity.

God *did* have a plan for me, and it *did* involve my facing this inconceivable agony. Though I felt myself tempted to ask the Father, like Jesus did in Gethsemane, to take this nightmare away from me and let me live beyond my death sentence, I ultimately conceded to trusting the Father—just as Jesus did—to carry me through *even death, itself,* if that would bring me closer to fulfilling what He wished of me. Somehow, despite everything I was facing, I knew everything would be okay…whether or not "okay" meant my forthcoming death. *Either way*, if I could just stop my world from spinning for five minutes and grasp some transcendent, godly, Christ-like thinking, I might be able to say along with Paul, "If I live, I live for the Lord; if I die, I die for the Lord, but whether I live or die, I am the Lord's" (c.f., Romans 14:8).

Beautiful words…but they are easier said than truly, deeply embraced.

I will be honest with you readers: There were countless times when my faith was exercised like a mantra, when I said the right words and prayed the right prayers even though my head and my heart were in conflict over the matter, like the first week after I was placed on chemo pills. My heart *knew* that God was Lord over my whole life, that He wasn't surprised by this diagnosis, that He knew what He was doing with me... and I kept those thoughts on repeat while I sank further into His Word and His presence like a frightened child to her daddy, knowing His love was very real and His provisions grander than any doctor.

Chapter Eleven

CHEMO...*THERAPY?*

When I started vomiting, with sickness coming out both ends, the "heavenly perspective" lens got a little difficult to keep peering through. With dehydration making me dizzy, and the "spinning" sensation in the room around me became a vertigo-level reality and not just a mental torrent, sometimes my glorious "trust in God" moments were slightly disconnected, faraway, and mechanical. I still believed the words I said and prayed, but it was understandably harder to *feel* His plan for me while this new drug made me more intimately familiar with the porcelain throne. When that mess took over my life, I had moments where I wondered if I had at some point become the wayward child that the Heavenly Parent was allowing to experience the hole she dug herself into with past sin.

If this *was* supposed to be a punishment for my former wrongdoings, it was working... Chemo-"therapy" (a misnomer if there ever was one, in my humble opinion) was very punishing, indeed.

The side effects of oral chemotherapy began immediately and got rapidly worse. I hadn't had any pharmaceuticals in my body for so long—not even Tylenol or over-the-counter medications—that when the intensity of *chemo* coursed through my veins, it was like going from zero to a thousand harsh side effects in a single weekend; the closest thing to hell a person can experience on earth.

My stomach twisted up in horrendous knots. I was like the woman who finds herself climbing to the height of a roller coaster's peak, knowing that the *second* it dove downward, she was going to lose her lunch. I lived in that state. Too many roller coasters in one day could make even the toughest of iron stomachs regurgitate the last meal all over the downwind passengers because human bodies can't handle continual, bouncy, jerky, lurching patterns of fast travel in every direction without a feet-on-the-ground break. But human bodies also can't handle going from no medications for *decades* to chemotherapy without some serious aftereffects, because, in its own unique, roller-coaster fashion, the body has been sent into shock…and in my case, there was no end to the ride. My feet would never be on the ground again as long as I was putting those drugs in my body. The nausea just went on…and on…and on…and meanwhile, my downwind fellow passengers—John, family, and friends—were incapable of doing anything to stop my coaster and get me off. They were forced to ride this crazy expedition alongside me (though I'm sure all of them would have traded being puked on over what they were about to face). Within days, I was placed on a prescription to quell the queasiness, but alas, that secondary drug did utterly *nothing* to subdue the torturous sickness, so the nausea and vomiting remained constant.

Within days, diarrhea joined the chorus of chaos. I will spare you readers from the dreadful details but suffice it to say that my frequent visits to the restroom involved sitting on the toilet with a bucket in my hands—when I wrote a few paragraphs back that it was "coming out both ends," I meant it literally. My bowels that had only weeks before been shut down were now getting a lot of movement, though nothing about the transition from "blocked" to "moving" could be called "relief." It was torment. The constant shifting, wrenching, writhing motion of my intestines under my nauseated belly was so concentrated that I wouldn't have been surprised to find out someone implanted a python into my pipes while I was under anesthesia for that abdominal biopsy. And though I know better than to ever think something that unrealistic would ever literally happen, my body certainly behaved as if a snake *had* been snuck in at some point…the cramping was beyond belief!

Of course, with all fluid intake being expelled in these ways, I quickly became dehydrated…and by that, I don't mean just "thirsty," although that applied early on as well. Doctors will tell you that by the time you're experiencing shifts in blood pressure, body temperature, heart rate, muscle strength, and/or cognitive function, the dehydration has become severe and possibly life-threatening. Every moment the condition is not treated is another moment that can lead to permanent damage to such major organs as the brain or kidneys. I couldn't keep anything down or in. While my entire body was wrecked from the chemotherapy, all fluids my family tried to get into my system—including drinks of all sorts, alongside smoothies, soups, crushed ice, and even natural juices from raw fruits and vegetables—were almost instantly expelled. (My sister, Laura, remembers occasions when they would spoon-feed me hydrating foods or liquids because I was getting too weak to care for myself. It would take *hours* to help me finish off only half a glass of a smoothie, just to have it ejected afterward.) A few days into this madness, when my medical team acknowledged I was drying up faster than a puddle in a Sahara Desert sandstorm and my blood was losing vitamins critical to basic bodily function, I was made to report to the emergency room for fluid IV drips and to the infusion center for iron injections. As I'm sure you have caught on by now, this was a horror-show for my itty-bitty, hide-and-seek veins: poking, poking, *POKING!*...endless, *relentless* digging and stabbing up and down my arms nearly every day.

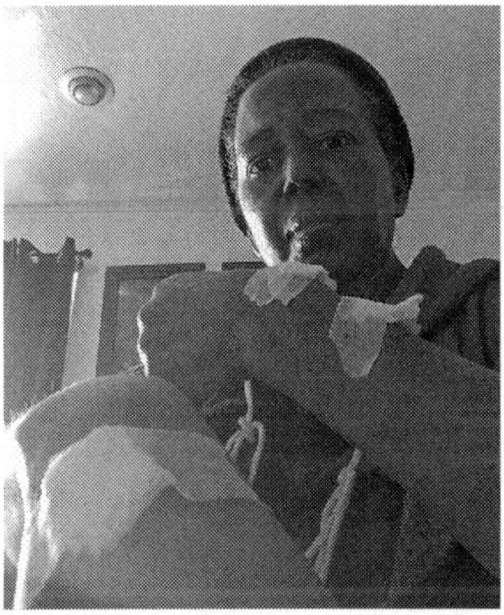

The day this picture was taken, I got lucky and only had to be stabbed *four* times with needles (one of the pokes is located just outside the photo)

But even if my veins were ideal—even if they were so amazing that nurses could have hooked them up to a firehose—the vomiting and diarrhea would have made short work of that hydration anyway, so I was just in misery around the clock, being repetitiously jerked away from the comforts of my own bed and rushed to ER (not a sick person's favorite place, to be sure...and I was starting to feel like I lived there).

Speaking of dehydration, one common side effect of chemotherapy is xerostomia or "dry mouth." You can drink and drink as much as you like, but your saliva glands are just not producing what they should be, so your mouth feels like a desert around the clock. There was, for me, no long-lasting relief from this. My mouth was *so* dry, and because saliva is how we break down food, no saliva obviously means food is not being processed properly by the body, so it was like eating flavorless sand. This, by itself, may not have been the end of the world, but a certain percentage of chemo-patients also come down with a case of mucositis or stomatitis, which is a condition wherein painful, white, ulcerous sores spring up inside the mouth as a result of inflammation of the oral tissues. I was one of the not-so-lucky patients in this regard, and those ulcers truly were *all over the place* in my mouth: inside my cheeks, along my gumline, below the gumline, all over my tongue, near the entrance to my throat, clustered on the backside of my lips, along the roof of my mouth…just *everywhere*, each one of them very large. Sometimes they were so big, and I had so many in one spot, that I couldn't distinguish where one ended and the other began; it was a huge, swollen, snow-white lump of canker-sore pain running the length of my lip or cheek like some bizarre mouth-leprosy. This made everything from eating, to drinking, to even speaking or swallowing an excruciating ordeal. The vomiting and diarrhea made it all the more important that I get, and *keep*, nutrients and fluids in my system if I had any hope at all of staying alive for long, and my family kept trying to get me to eat or drink to stay as healthy as possible, but they just didn't understand how badly those sores hurt! If a person were to take the most painful canker sore or cold sore they've ever had, multiply its size by ten, then multiply the sore itself by twenty and pepper them all throughout the inside of the mouth, and then zap all the saliva away and render the mouth so parched and void of moisture that the tiniest chewing/speaking/swallowing movement was like sandpaper grating against an open wound…they might have the very beginning of a guess as to how agonizing this condition was.

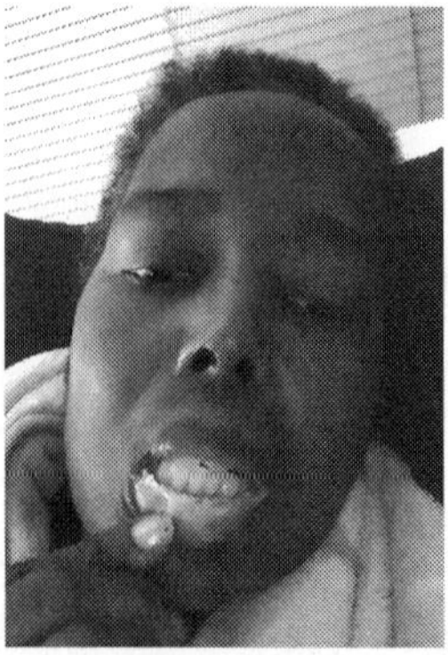

Mouth sores;
pictures just don't do it justice

All the while, food had no taste at all, so there wasn't even the standard appetizing quality that might push a person past the pain for a bite or two to indulge in their favorite flavors. In no time, I was dropping weight far faster than any doctor would deem healthy. Twenty pounds... thirty pounds...sixty pounds...ninety pounds... I was wasting away.

As gross as it is to say, one might take a single look at my bed sheets and assume all the weight I had lost was through the skin-shedding. Not literally pushing a hundred pounds in just peeling skin, of course, but chemotherapy burns your skin so bad that it's similar to a snake shedding its skin: Huge sections at a time peeled away and left behind. I would make jokes about getting a free exfoliation package from Western medicine, but outside of my attempts to let humor carry me when tears were my only other option, it really wasn't funny. Thankfully the skin peeling issue remained mostly limited to my legs and feet, but to those who sunburn easy and then peel: imagine one of those episodes that never ends and, just when you think you don't have any skin left to shed, your chemotherapy burns another layer, and it starts all over again. It was awful.

Then came the dizziness. Emotionally *and* physically, my world had been ceaselessly whipping about from the urgent care trip forward, but this chemotherapy dizziness was a whole new level. The room didn't *just* "spin," it gyrated, pulsated...throbbed around me, blasting my senses with surreal and overwhelming sights and sounds that wouldn't stay still or quiet long enough for me to interpret what I was taking in. If I ventured down the hallway or to the restroom, I had to hold the wall to steady myself from falling to the floor—which is odd to me now, looking back, because even the very walls felt like they were swaying under my touch and *nothing* was steady enough to lean on, really. Once I had entered the dining room, living room, or bedroom, it was all I could do to arrive at a piece of furniture I could lower myself to before my face bit the carpet.

And, not surprisingly, with as sick as I had become, there was the element of weakness as well. Falling to the floor or the ground was a serious issue since I didn't know if I would be able to get back up, that much was true, but it went beyond that to threatening my environmental stability as well. Not even a week into chemotherapy, I could no longer perform the most basic household functions, and the clean house I had always kept was becoming neglected. Those dishes I had kept on top of daily were soon stacking in the sink, accumulating that funky, slimy film characteristic of sour dishwater; laundry was piling up and getting that "old, wet towel" smell; toilets, showers, sinks, and faucets were starting to look dingy and dull; layers of dust, crumbs, hairballs, fuzzies, dirt, and crud gathered in corners, cracks, and between carpet fibers all throughout the floors that were no longer swept, mopped or vacuumed; and obviously, my bed wasn't getting made every day because it had now become my home. Yet, my family was so focused on tending to *my* needs that a messy house was the least of all evils and we wouldn't have had it any other way; who would prioritize sweeping crumbs and wiping down countertops when I was alone in the back room starving, thirsting, and wobbling my way to the toilet for the thirty-seventh purging or dry heaving that day? (As I mentioned briefly prior: The dogs were always fed, and their needs were tended to, thank goodness! Though I'm sure they missed my wrestling, even if I had felt up to it [which I didn't], John wouldn't have let me venture outside because, as weak as I had been, falling on the cement driveway and sustaining a head injury at the worst of times was a real concern.) Furthermore, we couldn't just accept assistance from anyone in our community who wanted to help us out by preparing meals or cleaning up around the house because COVID-19 was all at large and my immunity was so compromised that a single germ could have been the death of me. Thus, my home environment—that same set of surroundings that drove me bananas whenever clutter began to collect or something wasn't recently picked up or wiped down—was closing in on me in a whole new and profound state of upheaval and isolation. It might not seem like that big of a deal when compared to all I had going on in my body, but something about my former place of *comfort and safety* becoming a topsy-turvy, foreign prison to me added a layer of psychological insecurity atop my mortal vulnerability.

It didn't help that the only escape I had was to go see doctors and get the latest updates on how my death was progressing along. Though great lengths had been taken to make the environments of the medical clinics and facilities the most comforting atmosphere for patients—and that showed, especially in the "luxury hotel" cancer institute—one can only take so many trips to the doctor before even the very sight of those buildings a half mile away causes dread. I had switched from the "find it and diagnose it" phase of cancer treatment to the "chemotherapy maintenance" phase, which involved all of us watching to spot what damage chemotherapy was potentially doing to me, hoping all the while that the benefits outweighed the harm. The way they determine that is—of course, you guessed it—more blood labs. Every trip to have my blood drawn was an enormous hassle, and it would take *all day* between the labs, the doctor's review of the labs, and the near-certain follow-up trip to the infusion center to receive more needles in the arm for blood transfusions or whatever supplement shot was required to correct low numbers. It took a *minimum* of three or four blood-draw attempts alongside tourniquet adjustments and fist-making to get a single usable vial or IV link. My arms were bruised everywhere, deeply enough to leave lasting marks that were very noticeable from a distance, even for my dark skin tones. Between the bruises, the nausea and vomiting, the skin peeling, and the dizziness, I perpetually looked like the stumbling town drunk who just lost in a back-alley brawl...though outer appearances were certainly the least of all my worries.

It's true that I didn't care what I looked like in those days. Many people who have been through chemotherapy would agree with me that patients are far too ill to lose what little sleep they have left worrying about how "attractive" or "presentable" they are to the rest of the world around them. It's like a woman in hard labor asking her obstetrician between pushes whether she looks "hot" in her hospital gown; apart from a hysterical joke or a comedy sketch on Saturday night television, that's just... not a thing. But there is a significant difference between *vanity* and *vitality* in one's appearance, and chemotherapy patients know exactly what I'm talking about. Nobody cares if you didn't put on your foundation, contour powders, blush, and lipstick before you left the house. But when that natural radiance and glow that accompanies healthy skin has disappeared, leaving that ashen-grey pallor of imminent death in its place, *everyone* cares, and for good reason. In the context of cancer treatment and the sickest days a person has ever lived, vanity is superficial and shallow, but vitality is life, health, and wellbeing. Losing all your hair within a couple months feels like a threat to survival, and even, perhaps, one's dignity—especially because of the widespread associations between complete hair loss and cancer on almost every cancer-awareness billboard and poster in the nation. When chemo-chemicals render you bald almost overnight, it feels as though you've become a walking advertisement or "poster girl" for a new drug or a sick-people club. A woman's hair is her "glory," according to Scriptures (1 Corinthians 11:15), and though I'm aware that statement has inspired a lot of interpretational debate (modern head coverings, appropriate hairstyles for churchgoing women, and even some teachings that link female authority or anointing to what a woman wears or grows atop her head), I personally feel happy accepting the statement in its most basic simplicity: A woman's hair is her glory, her crown, an outward picture of her internal splendor...a part of her feminine *vitality*. In some African American communities (including mine), a woman's hair is her crown, and dreadlocks are considered one of the purest expressions of black identity, history, spirituality, and pride. The shape, density, and texture of African hair is unique from other races, and though many other cultures celebrate dreadlocks (and they look equally as cool on everyone, in my opinion), it comes very natural to us to grow them. It's like a second nature, the way the hair develops a sort of "directional memory"; I have to retwist the roots about once per week as new growth comes in, but after I have, the hair "remembers" that new direction and naturally maintains the shape from then on. My beautiful dreadlocks were a part of me, not because I'm vain, but because this was one of the ways I liked to express my African identity. When I woke up one morning to retwist the new growth and a full dreadlock strand fell into my hand, I knew the day was soon approaching when I would have to face losing it all. Within the next few days, another strand fell out while I was in the shower, and yet another was discovered on my pillow. It pained me, but I knew I had a very limited window of time to preemptively get ahead of the new 'do and make it look intentional before I started to resemble...well, precisely what I was: a cancer patient whose head is balding one giant chunk at a time.

It all had to go. I convinced myself it was "*just* hair" that would all grow back—and technically, it *was* just hair and it *would* grow back—but it was more to me in that moment, when I sat at the dining room table and let my son shave it all to the floor. It was a piece of *me*, a slice of my individual self-expression and identity, that was being cut off. And though it was my decision—and again, *technically* it was—it wasn't really "my" decision because I had no choice. It was a sentence pronounced upon me in the court of the infamous Judge Cancer, and Chemo was the sole juror. My pretty dreads were stolen from me, not freely given, so when they were chopped off—when a piece of *me* was chopped off—I allowed myself the grace to show some emotion and let go of a few tears. Several people suggested that I keep the dread strands because they could be reattached to fresh growth at a later time when my treatment was completed. However, I ultimately went with the advice of my son, who noted that this hair strewn about the dining room floor represented a sick woman. Someday, if I actually did pull through all of this, reattaching those dreads would be like binding a piece of an old, sick, dying woman to the "glory" of my head. At this point, it wasn't looking very promising, but in my wildest imagination, if I ever found myself lucky enough to be gazing into the mirror and planning a *future* look for my hair again, I would want it to symbolize just that: a *future*.

March 2021, sporting a headful of my own natural, freshly unbraided (and therefore "curled") dreadlocks just a few months before diagnosis

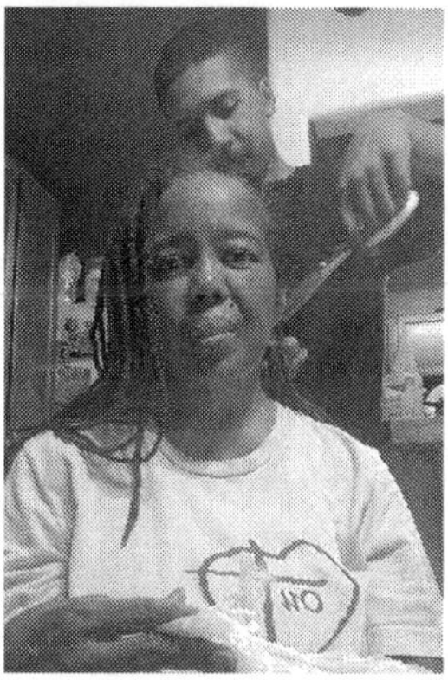

September 2021, reluctantly letting my son Isaac cut it all off

July 2021, still reeling from the news here, though my dreadlocks had not yet begun to fall out

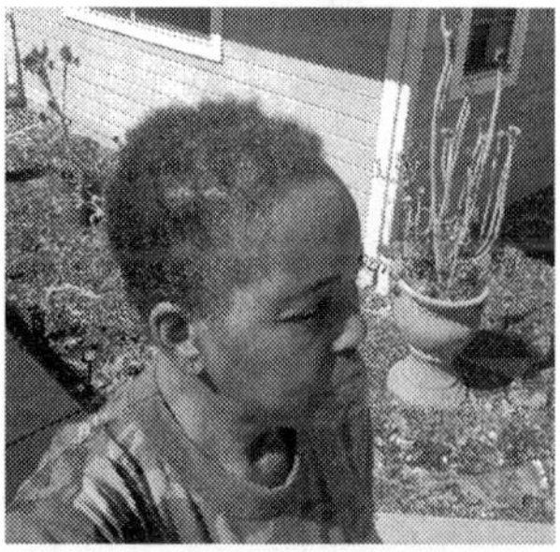

Just after having the dreadlocks cut; thinning became even more visible after this photo was taken

As the days passed, scary moments became the norm for all of us, such as the days my hemoglobin dropped dangerously low and I had to receive blood transfusions. (The hemoglobin is a protein within our red blood cells that transports oxygen wherever needed throughout the body. Low hemoglobin means low oxygen in the blood, which is bad news.) I was grateful for the blood that someone else had opened a vein to provide for me, of course, but I also found it a little unnerving: taking someone else's body fluids into my own, not knowing who they were, how they lived, or what, if anything, might be in that blood that the screening process may have missed just before approving it as a viable donation… Nevertheless, the transfusions saved my life on multiple occasions and I am eternally grateful for those men and women who braved the needle for those who need what they have in abundance.

On other occasions, it was the watchful eye of my sister Laura that saved my life—like the time my potassium levels dropped to 2.4 millimoles per liter (3.6 to 5.2 is the normal range), which is life-threatening as it can stop or severely damage the heart. Because she had been given clearance to view my lab results, she caught this concern even earlier than the experts had, and proceeded to bombard my doctor's office with phone calls in hopes that they would send over a prescription-strength potassium supplement for me. The following day, when Laura's messages had not effectively been delivered to the proper channels, I was back in the hospital, probably close to death again, but because Laura knew what I needed, my critically low potassium was identified right away and dealt with quickly.

Other scares weren't as smoothly addressed, like the time my stomach swelled to the point I looked pregnant and I had to go in and have *four liters* of fluid drained. (And for those who can more easily imagine it this way: four liters is just a little more than a gallon—so imagine that gallon of milk in the top of your fridge filled with cancerous fluids and stuck in the belly…)

Ascites, commonly referred to as "chemo belly," is a condition in which fluids build up in and around the abdominal area as a result of inflammation caused by cancer cells. Though Dr. Ibrahim didn't directly say at the time why she felt it was necessary to delay having the fluids drained from my abdomen, I later came to understand it was because she felt the risks of having my belly punctured with the draining needle—and therefore exposed to outside contaminants while my immunity was already so drastically compromised—might outweigh the benefits of having the fluids removed. I continued to trust her expertise, but the problem escalated to epic proportions. I couldn't sleep in any normal position: on my side, the enormous protrusion caused severe irritation and tenderness, pulling everything including my skin like a giant water balloon wobbling and stretching sideways; on my back, the fluids crept up from within and made me feel like I was drowning (which is a bizarre sensation, knowing your head is above water but your lungs are *not*); and obviously, laying on my stomach was out of the question. Shortly into this season of pseudo-pregnancy, circumstances grew wildly out of control. Not only was it perhaps the most incredible discomfort I've ever felt having to learn to sleep sitting up while I was sicker than a dog and needed deep rest more than ever, it just *kept* expanding, bigger and bigger, with no sign that it would ever slow down, let alone stop or shrink. At least with a legitimate pregnancy, a woman has nine months to take this bulge in feasible increments; my chemo belly came on hard and fast. It started the size of a baby bump, and continued to steadily increase in size until I appeared five months pregnant, then six, then seven...by the time I looked like I was eight months into carrying twins and about to simply burst, I begged my oncologist to *please* do something about it. She consented, and when I reported to the gastroenterologist in charge of the draining procedure, he notified me that the fluid buildup had already spread to my heart—which, I would come to find out, increased the risk of imminent heart failure or death, if the matter wasn't swiftly rectified. On the other hand, he couldn't justify removing the buildup around the heart because, he explained, it was in a precarious spot and drainage with his equipment near that area would be too dangerous. He seemed confident that proceeding with abdominal draining would indirectly fix the problem; all remaining fluids in the chest would dissipate and absorb into the rest of the body once the belly was drained and that pressure was relieved. By the grace of God, he ended up being correct...but it wasn't lost on me that we caught this in the nick of time. I easily could have gone to sleep in my horrible sit-up position one day and never awakened to meet another. I can't imagine my family going through this whole cancer journey with me, all the way up to this juncture, just to see me die of a pointless heart attack or equivalent!

There was no doubt about it—Dr. Ibrahim's warning was accurate. Chemotherapy is "brutal": an every-day, night-and-day, head-to-toe, mind-body-soul kind of brutal.

How ironic that the name of the treatment that causes *all this* includes the word "therapy."

(In hindsight, looking back, man oh man… Wouldn't it have been so nice if there was something *natural* I could have taken instead? Something that, oh, I don't know, *God made*? Yeah. "God medicine." That would have been amazing. Heh.)

So…yes, I absolutely and irrefutably believed in, and trusted, God to carry me through this whole painful, frightening journey—that much is undeniable. But how that assuredness manifested during chemo treatment is not as glamorous or inspirational as some readers may have hoped to hear at this point in my story. I *wanted* the strength and confidence of the apostles' "heavenly perspective"—I prayed for it, and I had faith that it was very real and beneficial!—but conditions such as vomiting, diarrhea, arm-poking sessions that lasted forever, and trips for emergency fluids and critical supplement shots aren't really conducive to poetic, inspirational, faith-filled moments of beauty and communion with the Divine.

At least not at first… I would have days coming soon when I realized that the perspective I was trying to activate within me thrived in conditions just like these (and those far worse), proving to be *precisely* the right time for communion with the Divine… And just when all these concepts regarding God and my reliance upon Him got too fuzzy for me to sort out in my own logic, the Father would send a signal that He was in control and present during my battle, like the day Cislyn came to pay a visit.

Chapter Twelve

"GOD IS *GOING* TO TOUCH YOU"

My husband, the "guard dog" of our home during COVID-19, didn't allow just anyone to bring their germs into my environment, but he did allow visitations from those we trusted well enough to be careful about what they were exposing me to. Cislyn was one such guest.

I had known this blessed woman since I was a teenager. Mary, my younger sister, reached out to Cislyn to let her know I was very sick, and she made time to come and pray with me and my sisters a few weeks into my chemotherapy. As exhausted as I was, I felt a stir of excitement when I saw her tall frame slip through the doorway, appreciating the beauty of her exceptionally dark skin as it contrasted against her bright smile and the whites of her kind, comforting eyes. In lieu of probably never seeing the beaches of Dominica again, having her nearby was like having a piece of home delivered to my bedside.

As one might expect, the first half of her social call was spent bringing her up to speed about the six-letter assassin working his way throughout my tissues: my diagnosis, how I was feeling, what our expectations were regarding the next steps in treatment, and so on. By this time, my mouth sores were beginning to heal quite nicely because of the prescription-strength mouthwash my doctor put me on, so we were able to converse without too much pain. After the general updates, Cislyn shifted the focus to prayer. With her beloved Caribbean accent that was so homey and familiar to me, she guided us into a sweet conversation with God, petitioning for His far-superior, supernatural healing to intervene on my behalf so I would not be reliant upon only that which mankind had concocted. At a pinnacle moment mid-prayer, she stopped speaking to God directly, turned to me, and stated as a matter of absolute fact—as if it were a "done deal" arrangement that had already been settled in the supernatural realm that she was somehow more privy to than the rest of us—that God was going to bring a miraculous, healing touch to my body.

"He's *going to* touch you," Cislyn said, as if any doubt in this moment, no matter how reasonable, was a laughable absurdity.

Immediately after those words were uttered, she slipped back into prayer, directing her words to God again until the petition for my health and safety came to a natural and sweet conclusion. I closed my eyes worshipfully and thought about the vastness of God while marinating on Cislyn's words.

God is "going to" touch me, she said...

"Going to." Period. Not "might"; not "could"; not "if it's His will to"; not "we know He has the power to if He should so choose"... He was "going to" touch the disease flowing through my veins, and in context of the surrounding prayer, it was clear that this "touch" was one of healing.

On any other occasion, I might be tempted to go back and forth in my thoughts, entertaining the war between Faithful Lynette and Fearful Lynette, wondering how Cislyn could feel so confident about the statement she made, wrestling with whether she could be right or wrong, wondering if she had properly understood the promises of Scripture, or any number of curiosities that would have made it about *her*. But on this particular day and in this particular moment, it didn't even occur to me to engage in the ping-pong match born from within my own human psychology...

"She" said it—but really, "He" said it *through* her, and I recognized that for what it was, and then proceeded to accept and receive it as a promise that God was doing something wonderful with me. And in a matter of time—short, finite, temporal, earthly time that, at its longest, is measured to be nothing lengthier than a "vapor" sighting in biblical terms (James 4:14)—I was going to know exactly what that wonderful thing was.

The Gaither Vocal Band's old song "He Touched Me" came to mind, and I sang it like a promise over my life: "He touched me, oh He touched me, and oh, the joy that floods my soul; something happened, and now I know, He touched me and made me whole." Before I had reached the end of the chorus the first time, Cislyn and my sisters joined me. None of us are or ever were professional singers, but this blend of confident, peace-filled, promise-claiming vocals left more of an impression upon me than the grandest of choirs performing live within the acoustically unparalleled walls of the Royal Albert Hall. Something in the atmosphere was shifting...and we all felt it.

Cislyn, the beautiful woman God chose to speak through when announcing my forthcoming healing

Tears welled up, escaping my eyelids and racing to my chin as I recognized the presence of God, Himself, entering the room to fellowship with His daughters. A *powerful* feeling of peace and assurance suddenly broke through and shattered the walls of anxiety I had built within myself. It flooded my mind, my heart...my very soul—inaudible whispers on repeat confirming: I *would* be healed. It was a future reality that I could count on, lean on, rest in, and look forward to.

A done deal. Healing was *mine*.

We kept our voices lifted to the heavens in worship of the Creator who made me—the One who designed my body to be disease-free and to self-heal when compromised by the condition of sin that mankind continually ushered into this planet's atmosphere from the time of Adam forward. God's original plan did not include cancer. Before rebellion was introduced to our world, the human body and brain were perfect. But when we chose to put the temptation of the serpent above God, we destroyed bodily perfection and initiated an entropic spread of decay throughout the universe.

Readers of the Bible know what happened next…

He—the same God who was innocent of the Genesis malady—put forth a plan to reverse it and give us *back* the power of life through the sacrificial blood of His only Son. Jesus' arrival, ministry, and work here on our soil two thousand years ago gave us access to God directly, and if anyone had the authority to kick cancer where it hurts and give me the gift of life, it was *Him*.

It would be poetic if I could tell you readers that I sang a chorus of a pretty song, had an epiphany, brought every element of my cancer treatment into alignment with the will of God, and "got better overnight," but I'm convinced that's not what was supposed to happen. (If you've read the introduction, you may recall I believed I was supposed to experience both sides of the cancer story so I could compare them and speak out about the one that wins…) I believe that I was on a journey involving many *multiple* epiphanies regarding what steps God would want me to take in radical obedience to Him, and if I had been shown the Father's ultimate finish line in this moment, I may not have been strong or desperate enough to run the race He wanted me to run. I might have made a beeline for the goal, missing crucial, faith-building pitstops along the way, and He knew that. So, instead of slapping me upside the head with the obvious "do this; then that" directives, God simply let me *feel* Him there beside me as Cislyn hit the grand-slam homerun.

First, she followed the Spirit's prompting to tell me God was going to heal me, and *then* she told me exactly how that healing would come about…

…Though none of us knew that at the time.

"You know, they told me twenty years ago I was going to die from cancer," she said, leaning back and tucking a cute black curl away from her eyes. "I wasn't going to make it, they told me."

I stared, stunned and in wonder that this had never come up before.

How had I known this woman almost my whole life and never learned that she stared death in the face and won?

"Yeah, and I'll tell you another thing," her thick accent added an edge of confidence and determination, "they said I had a fifty-fifty chance of survival with chemotherapy. I said, 'Fifty-fifty? All that expense and pain and it's not even guaranteed to work past a half-chance at life?' So, I figured I had nothing to lose, planted a garden in my back yard, switched to a completely vegan diet—only fruits and vegetables and herbal teas—and never did go through with the chemo plan."

Cislyn went on to explain that, not only did she decline the pharmaceutical approach to cancer, she literally never went back to the doctor for a follow-up. Ever. *Not once*. Not even to determine if the cancer had ever disappeared or if she was simply still carrying it around casually.

"For all I know, I might still be living with it, like other people who live with chronic illnesses, but I knew," she paused, blinked, and shook her head, "I *knew* they were not going to put that poison in my body, and now I'm in my seventies and I feel just fine."

Perhaps God intentionally allowed a pair of scales to linger over my eyes—like He did with Paul in the book of Acts—blinding me from fully comprehending how all of this so obviously connects. Maybe He wasn't the reason behind my impaired vision at all, and I simply remained too distracted by my own human problems to completely tap into a clear signal from Him and see what I was supposed to see…? I honestly don't know for sure why I didn't realize what was right in front of me in that moment, but looking back, it's so obvious now: 1) a promise of healing, followed by 2) instructions for organic restoration through God's soil and plants—all delivered through a walking, breathing, personal example of a woman with my same ailment who experienced exactly this 1-2 combo and lived to tell the testimony of its efficacy. All I can say is that, while I was contemplating God's wonderful and perfect plan for *my* healing, I saw chemotherapy as the vehicle within which that healing would be brought.

Maybe the reason I didn't connect the dots completely that day could be because of the way Cislyn articulated her follow-up care. Something in how she put it—cancer possibly still lingering within her even now, though nobody would ever know—made me all the more determined to kill the infected tissues within me in the most aggressive way possible, and to do so permanently. That goal, in this moment, still wore the "chemo" label, as that was the answer as per the experts I had spent so much time with lately. In the moments following God's presence permeating the atmosphere and bringing supernatural confidence to my heart, soul, and mind, I clung to the most familiar, celebrated solution to my problem.

This chemotherapy is going to work. I thought to myself. *I'm going to beat this.*

Later on, when I would be prompted by the Spirit of God to completely abandon all manmade pills, infusions, or drugs in exchange for His own perfect medications—the healing ingredients He engineered into the soils of this very earth on the day He made paradise—I would be mature enough to do so because of the stacked layers of confirmation gained during my seasons of impaired spiritual vision. So, I am not ashamed or embarrassed to admit that I had scales over my eyes that day. Those scales would come off in God's perfect timing, at precisely the point in my journey *He* wanted them to, when I had learned all the lessons *He* wanted me to learn, and not a moment before.

Meanwhile, some of those lessons ahead of me would make everything I'd gone through up to this point look merely "mildly uncomfortable" by comparison…and this next chapter in the journey would make me infinitely grateful for the good-news promise of healing that God sent through Cislyn that day.

Chapter Thirteen

THE DAY I DIED

Nothing could have prepared me for what transpired at a "routine checkup" scheduled just before Thanksgiving. I had been through so much already, and I continued to rely on God to temper the metal I was made of through His Word, prayer, beautiful sounds of worship (through such anointed vocals as CeCe Winans), and a radical, sold-out belief in the promise of healing. But for as strong as I had no doubt become, it was about to be illustrated just how far my horrific physical condition had advanced…

…And just how mortal I really was in the battle against it.

That morning was unreal. From the moment I rolled out of bed, something just wasn't right with me. The incredible physical fatigue and mental disorientation that I experienced snuck up on me without warning. Both my body and mind had, while I slept (evidently), contracted a kind of weird, lethargic, slow-motion sloth-syndrome straight out of bizarro-land. The last time I had prepared to leave the house, I was "tired," but *this* level of deep, bottomless exhaustion was now the new standard by which all weariness for the rest of my life would be compared. Never had I felt that weak, drained, lightheaded, or faint.

And what was going on with my brain? Why couldn't I string two sentences together in my mind? Even if I could snap my finger and force my body's strength and speed to return, what would I *do* with that physical strength and speed other than stand and stare blankly at a wall? At this rate, asking me to accomplish any more than that was an intense challenge. To some degree, I didn't even know where I was. Don't get me wrong—I knew I was "at home," but the word, the very *concept* called "home," was floating above me like an elusive mystery I couldn't connect to. "Home" was a happy place, a good and *safe* place, but suddenly I was a stranger to whatever that meant.

Nobody had told me about "terminal restlessness" or "terminal delirium," which is a neuropsychiatric condition that typically impacts cancer (or hospice) patients in the last twenty-four to seventy-two hours of their lives. Symptoms involve considerable disorientation, confusion, lack of awareness, odd interactions with surroundings, disruptions in attention, and inconsistent speed in body movements, just to name a few. Meanwhile, as it directly affects the patient's brain and comprehension—and by extension, his or her capability to recognize the onset of symptoms for what they are—it's not unusual that a patient will be in the advanced stages of this delirium while simultaneously unaware of its fatally serious implications. Such was the case for me. I generally knew "something" was wrong, and in my most lucid moments it rattled me deeply, but then, a moment later, I would be back on Mars where I didn't have the cognitive function necessary to know *what* was wrong, what to do about it, or how dire it truly was. I just kept thinking what I was experiencing was at the extreme end of "common chemotherapy side effects."

But I'm not going to lie...these were purely and unadulteratedly the most severe "side effects" I had faced yet. If a paramedic had approached me while I was getting ready for the appointment that day and asked me how many fingers he was holding up, I *would have* been able to provide the correct answer eventually, but first I would have to: remember what "fingers" were, then take a second to locate them in front of my face, then recall what it was I had been asked about these hovering things called "fingers" in the first place, then count each of them before proceeding to the next... The cerebral links between my brain and body on one hand and the way my brain and body interacted with my environment on the other had been cut, like a bad connection during a phone call when neither party can properly communicate with the other—just static and garbled bits of sentences. Every physical motion I made required Boston-Marathon-levels of energy to execute, and my ability to stay focused on any one thing for more than a second or two was waning fast. I could barely move, and things shifting around at normal speed within my vicinity was bombarding and otherworldly—all of this being in addition to many of the chemotherapy side effects that had been plaguing me from the beginning, like nausea, dizziness, etc. With this new added layer of confusing symptoms, my morning "routine" was anything *but* routine...and it would be the same for the "routine checkup" I was about to report to.

While at the mirror, my sluggish arm lifted to reach for my toothbrush, but it took forever to make contact, and once I had it in my hand, I had to concentrate on why I was holding it. The way the material atmosphere around me flashed back and forth between moments of recognizable reality and moments of abstract surreality rendered a near-comical rhythm in the universe, as if the world, itself, was "speaking caveman":

Toothpaste...on...bristles...

What is happening to me?

Toothbrush...under...water...into...mouth...

This unfamiliar, plastic, tooth-cleaning gizmo was now between my cheek and the gums. Wasn't that where it was supposed to be?

Flash.

Yes, that's where the toothbrush goes, for crying out loud. I'm brushing my teeth, and here in a minute I'll need to get dressed so John and I can leave for the routine appoi—

Flash.

What was that thing I was holding again? What was I doing standing here?

Flash.

Good grief, Lynette. Get a move on! Brush your tee—

Flash.

Funny little plastic stick in my mouth...

I had never moved so slowly in my life. (Thank goodness my mouth sores had healed; I didn't have to spend extra time brushing around ulcers.) My eyes staggered from object to object, unable to remain on any one thing longer than a moment or two before I had to blink—and each blink required Herculean strength to pry my eyelids open again. My breath was labored as I pressed the bristles in against the gumline and began brushing in drowsy, droopy circles. Feeling my balance teeter off-kilter, I leaned into the counter for support, and as soon as I could bring my brain to tell my other arm to respond, I gripped the counter for added stability.

Just gotta...get ready, I managed to think. *Gotta go...see the...doctors.*

The room woozily swayed and bent around me as I held my feeble hand at the counter's edge.

Have I been drugged?

I knew I hadn't actually been drugged, as nobody in my family would have ever dreamed of slipping me something that wasn't on my list of approved medications, and they were the only people who had access to me. However, drugs would have certainly explained this otherwise-unexplainable, dreamlike sensation I was walking in. I had no idea at the time that this was what the beginning of the actual death event felt like for a cancer patient. Even in that very moment, I was dying. My body was failing me, giving up, throwing in the towel, and I was so desperately trying to carry out my daily routine. If I could just *get there*, the doctor might be able to tell me what this new sensation was.

By way of some unearthly miracle, I managed to finish with my toothbrush, rinse it, and relocate it to its holder. My eyes moved upward to my hair, which was little more than a buzz-cut since my son had snipped off my dreadlocks.

Flash.

My hair. Why was I looking at my hair? There was something I was supposed to be doing with it, wasn't there?

Flash.

You can forget about your hair, Lynette. Running a comb through that mess will have to wait until another day. Something very, very *strange is happening this morning and hair is most definitely not a priority. Just throw a cap over it.*

Flash.

What's a cap? Throw it…where?

The disorientation continued in this odd way, blipping in and out, back and forth, relentlessly. I had, of course, had a few "brain fart" episodes in recent weeks, but it was increasing rapidly now, keeping me from the most basic steps in daily preparation that I had carried out every day of my life since I graduated out of diapers. The closer our departure time for that appointment came, the more this flashing phenomenon increased: I would know just what I needed to do, then I would be practically comatose in mass confusion, and all the while, I was too weak to accomplish anything.

And then there was clothing. Clothing would be necessary if I didn't want to get arrested for indecent exposure the minute I left the house. It was like it had just occurred to me for the first time, ever—a profound, mathematical epiphany: leave home + no clothes = bad. Begrudgingly, I dragged one foot after another into the adjoined bedroom.

Step…to…bed…

Put…clothes…on…

To add to the disorientation and confusion of my thoughts, I was now beginning to experience a distorted-perception syndrome known as *dysmetropsia* or, in lay terms, the "Alice in Wonderland Syndrome": Objects look and feel closer or further away than they are, and walls and floors (or the ground) appear as if they're going to swallow a person whole if he or she leans against or walks upon them. In my bedroom, the definite borderlines of objects blurred in and out of focus and melded together intermittently, while colors throughout the environment stretched over here, shrank over there, and bled into quite an intangible canvas. Shapes and surfaces were pliable and bendy where they should have been solid. For a second or two, I would feel convinced I had seen one object absorb another, but when I really studied the area, I would be back in my room again, everything where it should be.

What…what should I wear? It's cold outside. Isn't it? Yeah. I think…I think it's cold outside.

Sometime before the end of sixteen consecutive eternities, I had located a grape-colored pair of sweatpants, a black sweatshirt, and a grey, knitted hoodie-sweater that came down to the middle of my thighs, and then I sat down to dress myself at the edge of the bed.

One leg in—room pulsating; nothing is real; can't move a muscle.

Second leg in—feeling a little stronger now; celebrating progress.

Sweatshirt over the head—celebrated early; almost fainted; nearly fell; might've died; everything swirling…

Arms…through…the…

Where am I? What am I doing?

Flash.

Come on, Lynette, get dressed!

Flash.

Do what, now?

Arms through the…

I tried again to don my outermost layer, channeling all the power I had into my upper body until somehow, in some way, my sweater had been pulled on completely. Another Herculean blink brought me to reality and I knew it was time to head to the car.

Lifting my body to my weary feet and wobbly legs, I heaved one eternity-step after another out of the bedroom and into the hallway, holding onto every steady surface my shaky fingers could (pitifully) grab hold of along the way.

Something is really wrong, I managed to think in a moment of increased clarity as John rounded the corner to help me. *I don't feel right. Even for a woman who is dying in a couple months, this is extreme.*

I *was* dying—but not "in a couple months." Progressively, in that very moment, I was beginning my trip to the afterlife. I just didn't know it yet. John obviously observed something about me that alerted him to the seriousness of the situation, as he slipped my right arm up over his shoulders and placed his left arm around my waist to hold me up. Then, together, we made the painstaking, everlasting trip to the car.

Once I was seated and buckled in, I was finally able to deliberate on what I was experiencing instead of thinking about teeth, hair, or clothing, but it hardly mattered. I could only gather together enough mental concentration to identify one thing for certain: I was losing my mind.

The car started to move.

The trees look weird. What's wrong with them? They're pointy.

All the familiar visual stimuli from these Fresno-California surroundings that I had taken in daily for years was suddenly as nonsensical and exotic to me as a newborn fresh out of the womb. Traffic signs, plants, telephone wires lining the street, other vehicles alongside us on the road, words on buildings I had seen a hundred thousand times…*everything* was foreign—and it was scary-foreign, not exciting-foreign. Like I had just landed on an alien planet: Not only did I not know what these common objects usually meant within my own past experience and worldview, I couldn't compute what they even *were* or how they would interact with the laws of nature.

Every piece of optical data that my eyes were communicating to my brain was incoherent. The very fact that I was in a car, and it was moving, and I was moving with it, and we were going somewhere, and that somewhere was a cancer place, and that cancer place was going to have people in it that did things—it was all absurd and incomprehensible. I was trapped in the unthinkable limbo where silly nonsense and pretty, flying colors meets instant torrents of terror when flashes of rational thought broke through to the surface, telling me this was *not* a good development. And in addition to this new and mysterious psychological disarray, I was dizzier than ever and felt as if the first of many bouts of vomiting was perpetually just on the other side of my next swallow.

I closed my eyes at the beginning of the drive and kept them closed for the remainder of the trip—a decision that may or may not have helped my belly's quease-factor but did quiet down the chaos in my head somewhat.

When we arrived, I was greeted by a kind, young, and thankfully very strong medical assistant who, with John's help, lifted my withering body from the car and into a wheelchair. My "Alice in Wonderland" depth perception told me that if I put my foot on the ground without help, I was going to sink down into the concrete.

Oh, good. There's a helper guy here. He will make sure the parking lot doesn't swallow me. A wheelchair. That's probably wise.

If I couldn't even get out of the car by myself, then I couldn't be my own medical advocate any longer. That opportunity had passed, and now I was at the mercy of others to see what was truly going on with me under the surface or let me die. In a moment, we would be at the entrance to the facility, and thankfully, one concern managed to climb its way to the forefront of my confused mind with enough clarity that I could address it before it was too late: They were going to separate John and I because of some COVID-19 policy, but this time, I simply couldn't let that happen.

"He's gotta come with me," I said, gesturing to John. "My caretaker… I can't…do this alone today."

"Of course," the medical assistant responded. "We will get a caretaker sticker for him. It shouldn't be a problem."

I vaguely recall being wheeled through the front waiting room and into an elevator, and then my memory flickers and skips forward to sitting still during my vitals for a medical assistant dressed in black scrubs. She asked me how my day was going, and I want to say I merely offered a weak smile in response while she slipped the blood pressure cuff up and around my bicep. One swivel of her chair and a button-press later, the automatic cuff inflated, squeezing tight with a series of beeps, and then gradually releasing pressure with a hiss.

"Alrighty then, let's see…" The young girl's countenance was what anyone would expect at first: going about her usual duties, exchanging pleasantries, and chatting about the day. However, somewhere around two seconds or so into her analysis of my systolic and diastolic numbers, her expression changed, beginning with a stiff blink and a wrinkled brow, quickly growing into a wide-eyed stare of disbelief.

I looked at the monitor. My blood pressure was 60/40. Somewhere deep in the recesses of my mind, a warning alarm was blaring; those numbers were bad—*very bad*—but I couldn't remember why or what it meant. I knew John wouldn't leave me, but I couldn't see him anymore. He must have been behind me in that room somewhere. In any case, I don't know what his reaction to those numbers were.

"Let's try that again." The assistant nervously readjusted the cuff and pressed the button a second time.

As the cuff repeated its pressurization, the gut feeling that had been needling at me all morning climbed to high-alert. I still didn't know what was happening, but somehow, in the midst of my delirium, from the depths of absolute mental stupefaction, came a firm conviction that something *very* ominous and possibly even deadly was coming for me, closing in, curling around me, stealing the very oxygen from my lungs.

After another series of beeps and the subsequent pressure-release hissing sound, the monitor flashed the numbers, and again, it showed my blood pressure to be 60/40—a picture I just happened to catch a glimpse of in the split second before the medical assistant's scrubs smeared and blurred like a wet paintbrush being dragged across freshly painted acrylics.

What happened next took place *fast*, leaving me with nothing but flicker-memories blended with blank segments of time I can't account for—like bits of a shaky, antique film reel retrieved from the floor of a studio cutting room and glued together to form an incomplete and unstable motion picture of the next hour in my life: The room's bright light took on a few shades of gloomy yellow, and the outermost boundaries of my peripheral vision went solid black, restricting my eyesight to a circle straight ahead.

Was it just me, or were the edges of that circle narrowing by the second?

The medical assistant was saying…something, and then she abruptly stood and ran for the door.

Was the tile floor rapidly retreating from me? Or was it the other way around? Was I really flying up and away?

Concerned voices echoed from somewhere outside the door and, within another moment or two—or was it an hour?—the commotion had appeared in the room all around me in the form of zooming scrubs and medical gadgets. They zipped to the left, then blurred to the right—new people I hadn't seen before grabbing at my wrists and talking about something called a "pulse." Walls and floors warped into fish-eye-vision shapes, and objects all around me were bending, twisting, distorting...

Mid-ruckus, a familiar face suddenly popped into the center of the narrow tunnel I was now viewing the world through.

"Are you okay?"

It was Dr. Ibrahim, bent down to my level, with a serious, concerned expression as her eyes studied mine intensely. Latching onto the only thing I could make sense of in this instant, I willed myself to bring her into focus, pleading with fate that I would be able to communicate to her, even in *this* moment, when communication was a quickly evaporating concept. Everything and everyone else faded into the edges of my ethereal, peripheral kaleidoscope-of-chaos.

In that vulnerable moment, it was just me and Dr. Ibrahim—a tag-team in a ring-match against Cancer, facing the pinnacle moment in the final round, and I was down for the count. I could almost hear the proverbial referee preparing the invisible crowd for my forthcoming loss: *Ten...nine...*

"Please," I said, desperately trying to throw my weak voice into a volume that could be heard above the din. "Help me."

"No pulse," a voice blitzed from the side of the room somewhere. "We can't find a pulse."

Eight...seven...

Dr. Ibrahim jerked away as she acknowledged the shocking statement, and then brought her attention back to me swiftly. Her expression silently implored: "Stay with me, Lynette. Stay with me..."

Six...five...

"No, there *is* a pulse," another voice announced, this time from a mile away. "We have a pulse. It's weak. It's *very* faint, but it's there. Ma'am, can you stand?"

The question was directed at me, and my one-word answer would have to suffice.

"N...no."

I felt my body lift upward and back down as they placed me on the stretcher, one paramedic on each side, for transport. Medical terms like "Intensive Care Unit" and "critical condition" were being spoken all around me while the hallways and doorways blurred together in a smear that eventually—a few flashes later—became the interior of an ambulance. The next statement was not directed at me, but I heard it nonetheless as I was fading in and out.

"Good thing it's only a sixty-second drive to the ER on the same lot."

Four...three...

Another flash of nonreality passed and I was suddenly in a new room with a new male doctor, whipping about frantically and shouting orders.

"I need two pints of blood and two liters of fluids right away."

"I'll put in the order," some girl from somewhere called out, "and see how soon I can get those."

"Look at her," came the response from the new doctor as he pointed down at me. "Does she *look* like she can wait for an order? I need those items *stat*! Get them *now*!"

My tunnel of vision dramatically narrowed.

Though my brain was practically scrambled eggs by this point—and counting fingers was out of the question now—my *heart* was still in tune with my Savior. I may not have been able to put words into sentences, but from the very depth of my soul, I felt a prayer take root that defied all languages; a prayer that would never be limited to whether or not I could articulate with voice or word. My will, my deepest *yearnings*, manifested into a supplication that may not have been corporeal or physical, but the power of it growing within me in that very second was so strong it was palpable, rendering everything else in the room—including my survival—irrelevant. The connection between my soul and my Creator swelled within me, and I felt an inaudible prayer overcome and absorb all worry and concern for earthly things.

It's true that I had been expecting a miraculous healing from God, as that is what I had believed He promised me through Cislyn. However, I also knew that God was above every single human expectation, His will for His children was far superior to our own finite desires and longing, and more than anything else, we can't add a single day to our own lives on this planet unless He grants it. Ultimately, regardless of what I thought

He would do for me, I trusted *Him* more than I trusted my own interpretations of His thoughts and ways.

And, as a result, in that very moment, I surrendered…just like the Son had surrendered on the cross: Into God's hands, I commended my spirit. It was finished.

Two…one.

The invisible referee stopped counting, and the result was clear to all: TKO—total knock-out.

Here I come, Lord.

The tunnel closed and the ceiling floated away.

◆ ◆ ◆

Down the hall, a sweet, loyal, devoted, and handsome man was being handed the most terrifying news he would ever hear in his life. Though I wasn't there to personally witness John's countenance in this moment, I know his eyes were pleading with Dr. Ibrahim, begging for any words of comfort that would wake him from this bad dream, beseeching her for just a morsel of hope amidst this torrent of unbelievable agony. But alas, my poor husband would not get what he asked for.

Instead, Dr. Ibrahim owned her unfortunate position as the bearer of bad news like a champion, faced what she had to do with bravery, honesty, and integrity, and gave it to him straight.

"No, John, I'm so sorry. I don't think your wife is going to make it. Her organs are shutting down."

There was nothing anyone could do. The world was in the middle of a pandemic; to mitigate the spread of COVID-19, family members were prohibited from remaining beside their loved ones in the ICU; and my oncologist had just confirmed John's grandest fears: I was a goner, and that horrible moment John watched them wheel me away was the last time he would ever see me alive.

Beaten, defeated, and petrified, John drove to my sister's house and broke down.

Months later, I would hear my sister reflect back on the moment John arrived at her door. It was the only time anyone had seen him cry.

I love you, too, sweet John.

Chapter Fourteen

HERE IN... *THE TWILIGHT ZONE*

The English language is incredibly complex, versatile, and expressive, in part because it has been historically influenced by so many other root languages (Latin, German, French, Greek, Spanish, Old Norse, Italian, and several others). At present, there are well over two hundred thousand words in the English language, one hundred and seventy thousand of which are considered both current and common. There's also an enormous pool of euphemisms, figures of speech, idioms, phrases, clichés, and combinations of cultural terms that provide additional forms of expression beyond what one finds in an English dictionary.

Yet, despite such a vast vocabulary at my disposal, when I think about what I experienced in the three weeks following this trip to the ICU, I maintain that there are *no* words that honestly and accurately capture what those inexplicable days were like.

When I surrendered my spirit to God, I truly didn't think I was ever coming back, so waking up here on earth was, by itself, quite mystifying. I remember that moment, when my eyes were first fluttering open and a voice near my head said, "There you are, welcome back!" (It was the emergency room doctor, whose name I never knew, but whose decision to demand blood and fluids "stat" ended up saving my life. If I hadn't been so out of it, I would have asked about him and made sure to thank him later for those decisions he made on my behalf that day.) The lights above me, along with the edges of objects and surfaces around me, were no longer registering to me in that swirly, stretchy, Alice-in-Wonderland-Syndrome fashion. It really felt as though I *was* in that same body I had spent my life in thus far, but I didn't feel any pain, nausea, or other disturbances that I had grown so used to feeling since chemotherapy began. At least for the moment, all was calm and quiet compared to the commotion around me when the world went dark...but all was very corporeal and physical, too, as opposed to the supernatural or spiritual realm I imagined myself awakening in.

This wasn't heaven, and this doctor by my side wasn't God: The hospital ambiance was back, in full working order, with blinking lights, beeping machines, wires and cords trailing all over the place, and high-tech monitors all around. The white walls were fitted with thermometers, ear and nose scopes, sanitizer dispensers, biohazard waste receptacles, and convenience stations containing all sorts of miscellaneous accessories such as vinyl gloves, masks, and tissues. Calm voices from medical personnel could be heard from the hall or a corner of the room, murmuring about follow up care, blood pressure numbers, heart rates, medications, and an unending list of COVID-19-related symptoms manifesting in various rooms scattered about the wing. Utility carts on wheels were parked in a few places nearby, sporting clipboards with papers and pencils sitting atop multiple closed drawers.

Here I was, in the flesh God gave me from my mother's womb forward...

Alive.

How was that possible? I *had* died, hadn't I?

Yes, I did. In fact, I had...gone somewhere *else*.

It was an enormous building without a ceiling, with overcast clouds as if it had just rained and the sun hadn't yet reclaimed its proper place in the sky. I can't explain how I know this, but in this otherworldly place, linear time did not exist; therefore, I have no idea how long I was there. Other people were present as well, some talking in groups, others standing still and looking about, while many were walking in the same direction. Two of these people stuck out the most to me: a young, athletic male with brown, wavy hair, and a little girl who appeared to be enjoying a bright-white chiffon Easter dress with matching, ballet-style shoes. I never spoke to anyone directly, but, in a way that defies all explanation, I "felt" them...*all* of them. And there was no fear, anxiety, or worries of anything remotely attached to this life.

All I know from this short experience—and this much, I know for certain and with a confidence that wild horses could never pull out of me—is that *life continues after this.*

It's such a short story, a miniscule blip in the light of eternity, with so few details I can't even understand, let alone explain, parse, or pontificate about. But, despite the fact that my contributing narrative of this place is so menial and insignificant compared to the impact it had upon me, I'll never forget how huge this experience truly was. For as long as I live, I will always recall that feeling—that "knowing," for lack of a better word—that we are all so much more connected than we realize while we're here on this planet, going about our daily lives with worries, fears, and concerns so marginal compared to the bigger picture of the afterlife. With just the tiniest taste of that truth now an intrinsic part of me, it breaks my heart when I reflect upon how many people don't know how deeply connected we all really are.

But now I was back. In my body. In the hospital. In the room with noisy, flashy tech; wires in, on, and around me everywhere; and a doctor who returned me to this realm of existence so my days with John and the rest of my family *might* not be as short as it otherwise would have been.

No, it wasn't heaven, but it wasn't your traditional, everyday *earth*, either.

I can easily tell you what events occurred in what order, but it's the eerie, surreal *feel* of the experience that simply doesn't translate. If Rod Serling, the iconic host of the 1959–1964 *The Twilight Zone* series, had lived long enough to hear this part of my story and adapt it into one of his episode scripts, I can imagine how that intro might be...

Fade in from black, while the unforgettable *do-do-do-do* theme song loops in that eerie, 1950s "ghost over your shoulder" tone. The audience floats through space while the voiceover warns that we are "about to enter another dimension," a "fifth dimension" that lies directly "between science and superstition." Just after the door, shattered window, eyeball, doll, and ticking clock all pan across the screen, Serling appears, standing on the front steps of a hospital entrance to address viewers directly.

"Imagine yourself in a hospital bed, moments before death," Serling says, smoke curling upward from his cigarette. "Despite all efforts from a sincere and highly skilled medical workforce to keep you alive, you feel the grip of the afterlife pulling you from your body. Believing that you have lived a good life and are ready to meet your Maker, you succumb to the pull, giving yourself over to whatever wonderful mysteries await you in the great beyond. But when you awaken, you find yourself in a place that defies all descriptions of heaven, hell, or any other life-after-death domain conceived of in the mind of man. It is clear, however, by the speed at which minutes, hours, and days all pass, that you can expect to spend eternity here..."

The camera slowly pans up and over Serling's head, traveling through an open window and into a sterile hospital room. Situated in the center is a woman (that would be *me*), alone, confined to a hospital bed, with only her own disquieted angst for company. She keeps one eye on the door at all times, wondering who or what might come through it next. Serling continues to launch the episode in his classic, dry-but-chilling fashion.

"You are in another world, at times familiar enough to make you question whether you ever left the earth, yet consistently strange enough to convince you that you *have*. You watch and listen as the beings around you speak in hushed tones and conduct eccentric experiments on your body. Their faces are masked, their hands gloved, and the rest of their anatomy is covered head-to-toe in some advanced form of protective gear. As you begin to plan your escape from these new surroundings, you wonder if *they* pose a threat to *you*, or if it is *you* who poses a threat to *them*, here...in *The Twilight Zone*."

It would have made a great episode, and yes, this imaginary Serling intro actually does help to capture the feel of that atmosphere. It was just *so* otherworldly that a *Twilight Zone* style prologue to this season of my life is uniquely appropriate...

First, COVID-19 had dramatically changed the way a hospital would function for a while. Everyone's voices were continuously muffled behind masks that *also* served to hide something as critical to human interaction as facial expressions; not only was it impossible to hear what someone was saying half the time, but their true reactions throughout all conversations were concealed. I had seen masks, social distancing, and other examples of our society's response to the coronavirus before this point, of course, but this hospital was practicing virus-security on steroids! A single, harmless cough turned heads and prompted immediate fever readings while another wave of whispers rippled throughout the hallways regarding who was last placed in an isolated quarantine or on a ventilator. Many rooms on my floor housed patients with conditions that, in the past, would have justified a mere facial covering, but now, mid-pandemic, doctors and nurses were donning full-body "hazmat" (hazardous material) suits that looked like they came straight out of a TV show about a zombie apocalypse.

People everywhere were keeping as much distance as possible from others, and even our standard North American greetings like handshakes and hugs were now illicit, criminal acts. If someone forgot and reached out a hand or a pair of arms, the offender would receive the stare-down-of-death, now that connecting to another human through touch of any sort (apart from necessary doctor-patient care) was forbidden...and if these protocols weren't followed, as the news reminded us all every hour, the result could be fatal. Loved ones were strictly prohibited from visiting the hospital at all times—up to, and including, a patient's moment of death, which would now be experienced alone in order to guard other patients from the germs one might unsuspectingly carry in from outside.

The world *had to be* distant, cold, and isolating—and look like aliens chittering in space suits, with the only visible *human* feature being a creepy, emotionless pair of eyes leering out from behind protective gear—lest "we all die." It was an occasion for a Rod-Serling narrative if I'd ever seen one, even without taking into consideration whether I had died and come back.

And those days really did drag on and on...*aaand* on. At every point in my life prior I had been active, keeping busy both mentally and physically while I held down a full-time job, played the role of "soccer mom" (technically basketball and wrestling) while I ran my kids around, whipped up healthy meals, wrestled with the dogs, attended church or prayer meetings, only daring to slow down after long days of persistent activity. Even in the weeks leading up to this time, when I was too sick to be up and around back home, I had familiar things to look at and touch between visitors who would alleviate my loneliness, and if nothing else, I could entertain myself with my phone. None of that applied now. Because nobody knew that the "routine appointment" was going to end in a several-week stay in the hospital, I didn't pack a phone charger, and by the time the nurses tracked down my phone along with the other personal belongings that had been confiscated when I was rushed to ICU, the battery was kaput. So, not only was I without any way of communicating with my family through texting, calling, or email, I also didn't have smart-phone access to internet browsing, apps, or games that help pass the time.

There was an old-fashioned dial-out phone on the wall in the room, but it was mounted a distance away from me. I was very weak, so having phone conversations away from the bed was hard. I think I placed two phone calls, one each to my husband and sister, the whole time I stayed, and both times nearly knocked the wind out of me. By itself, the act of talking was like intense physical exercise and my body wanted to collapse back into bed only minutes into the conversation. Besides, neither my husband nor my sister would demand my release, which was where our talks kept going. They obviously wanted me to be safe and get the expert medical help I needed, while I wanted to come home specifically because I believed that was where true healing—*and rest!*—could happen. If even a pleasant discussion fatigued me, a tense dialog between me and my loved ones about my homecoming in these dire hours wouldn't benefit anyone, so we hardly spoke. It's accurate to say that I was wholly isolated. Other than those few phone calls, I was completely alone, my sole human interaction being the medical staff who, with their extreme protective gear, looked as though they were afraid to touch me. (They really were kind; I don't mean to diminish that. But when all I could see of these strangers were their eyes—while they tended to *every last inch* of me!—it was a vulnerable and surreal relationship there for a few weeks...)

Then there was the issue of sleep that made the draggy time so much worse: Nurses and doctors took every possible opportunity to emphasize just how important deep rest was to the body's recovery...but they did so while deep rest was simultaneously *impossible*. That is no exaggeration. I can't say it enough: I could not sleep in that hospital. *At all.* And that's not to say my body didn't try to drift off, because it did, rather constantly. But each time I felt myself coasting into slumberland, a machine alarm would go off, or a cord would get wrapped around something, or a nurse would appear to check vitals and administer meds, or an orderly needed to move me to a wheelchair and back to change the bedsheets, or a doctor would come with an update, or people would stand right outside my door and discuss someone else's deadly symptoms and corresponding treatment, or, or, or...

A part of me was thanking the Lord every time I looked at the clock and another hour had passed, because it was another hour of my life I wouldn't have to spend in that place...yet the other part groaned because nobody knew when I was ever getting out of there. How could I appreciate a "countdown to my departure day" when nobody knew what day that would be?

The clock—and therefore my dire thoughts along with it—just went on and on, which rendered all former concepts of time irrelevant. Waiting for insurance to kick in after my biopsies was a nightmare, but in this place, with family completely cut off and everyone looking like leering, hovering hazmat space invaders, my insurance wait felt like sweet dreams by comparison. A minute might be sixty seconds in reality, but there, in that hospital room I occupied alone, each second was an hour-long reflection of who I was, what I was doing there, and how I was going to get out.

Early on, nurses saw to fitting me with a heart monitor that would become quite the annoyance. Evidently, my heart had been racing at over one hundred beats per minute when I first arrived to the recovery room, requiring that I be watched closely for a while. That much I understood, but why did they have to use such a sensitive and faulty piece of equipment? From the first day through the entire three-week recovery period, if the cord traveling from my finger to the monitor got pinched, even ever so slightly, it would sound an alarm throughout that floor of the hospital telling the staff my heart had stopped. Nurses would come rushing in, only to discover that the cord had been compromised yet again, so they would adjust it over and over, each time waking me from potential sleep and bringing my body out of a comfortable position so that, five minutes later, we could start all over again with a false flatline. (Thank God my heart didn't *actually* stop there toward the end. The nurses might have drawn straws to see who would be the unlucky one who had to reluctantly "mess with faulty cords again" and find that, by the time they got there, I was long gone—a victim of the heart monitor that "cried wolf" one too many times.)

Comparatively speaking, however, that defective monitor was the least of my worries.

The first time I tried to use the restroom, I discovered my legs weren't working. I wasn't a paralytic in the traditional sense, and my limbs still registered the sensation of touch, but when I swung my legs over the edge of the bed in an attempt to stand, I discovered to my amazement that I couldn't put any weight on them at all. The weakness was simply egregious. Even though I wasn't the strongest I'd ever been a day or so ago when the Alice in Wonderland Syndrome hit and the world went wonky, I could still at least *stand*, but now, collapsing to the floor (and taking cords and monitors with me) was the only accomplishment that would hail from such an endeavor. It honestly felt like someone had swapped my real legs with giant fabric doll appendages while I was out. They *looked* like my tried-and-true limbs...but the instant I threatened to make them work for me, they revealed themselves to be fake, useless hanging sticks, good for nothing but appearances—an outer-shell façade to dress the hidden disease within, but not "legs" as I had come to understand the word.

After pressing the call button to the nurse's station and waiting until the end of infinity for a response from the short-staffed crew, I learned on a deeper level what happened: When vital organs start shutting down, the nurse explained, one of the body's chief self-preservation mechanisms involves sending all blood and strength to those parts of the body most directly associated to survival, such as the heart, lungs, brain, and so on. More simply put, the body sort of "preserves what it needs most," and walking was not one of those things, so this hospital stay was going to be harder than I thought.

Later, my doctor confirmed what the nurse told me, and further explained that my muscles had not received any direct damage, but my muscle memory was gone and I was going to need a lot of physical therapy to repair what this near-death experience had done. Physical therapy would "reactivate" the communication network between the brain and legs, reminding the body what walking is and how to do it...which, as I would soon find out, was also going to be a part of the criteria for my release.

Lynette Hill wasn't going *anywhere* until she could walk again. So, for the next several weeks, I would be forced every day to put my body through excruciating, agonizing pain in physical therapy sessions, among so many other disturbing developments, like the problems I was having with food.

One common side effect of chemotherapy that I was harshly suffering from by this point was the disappearance of taste. This can occur because of both the aforementioned dry-mouth effect, as well as general tissue damage that the drugs have done directly to and throughout the mouth. A dry-mouthed cancer patient will feel hunger pangs the same as anyone else, but when nothing has any flavor, it's like the brain interprets food as a foreign object; you may as well try to dine on a cotton pillow. (Yum…?) And just like the sleep the patient needs so bad but can't get in a hospital, real nutrients are desperately needed in the body to heal and repair from physical trauma or sickness, and sometimes hospitals are a little bit (or *a lot*) lacking in providing for this need.

I want to be very sensitive in how I approach the subject of hospital food. There are folks working extremely hard, all around the clock, in hospital kitchens whose hearts are truly devoted to helping make people feel better. They could have chosen literally any job or career in the world, including many options that *wouldn't have* exposed them to serious contagions and disease each time they get on an elevator to report to work, but instead they chose to cook for people who are too sick to tend to take care of themselves. These men and women put love in those mashed potatoes, not just butter. For this—their sweet, loving, and honestly heroic decision to help people in this way—I offer only my sincerest gratitude.

I likewise wish to take a moment to defend them in light of the most frequent insult: that "the food tastes bad." Honestly, ladies and gentlemen, we need to consider where we're at when we take a bite of *that* cafeteria food. We're in a hospital, not a five-star restaurant. If we want fine dining, we can go to a restaurant. One word: priorities. The kind folks in hospital kitchens are there to feed those who are unwell, not impress patrons' refined and expensive tastes. In fact, it's somewhat the opposite: They are challenged with designing a menu that will appeal to taste buds *universally*, across the board, to every ethnicity and age, while at the same time accommodating all food allergies and stomach sensitivities in a place where people already feel sick. The only way that could ever be accomplished is to keep all food options on the milder, blander side, so everyone from Johnny-Come-Lately living on exotic peppers to Gramma Sue who believes milk is spicy can eat what's served and hold it down well.

However, *taste buds* aside, there is a quality issue that begs to be challenged at this point, not only for the hospital I stayed at, but almost all of these facilities in the United States at least (if not the rest of the Western world). It's the same "feeding the sick" angle of this topic that makes me a little curious as to how the menu's ingredients are approved. Think about it: People are literally, physically dying in this place, and sometimes the only thing that stands between their death and another chance at the future is whether their flesh, blood, and bones receive the necessary vitamins, minerals, protein, fiber, and overall nourishment needed to recover and return to optimal function. Whereas it's true that some of these essential supplements can be acquired through pill or powder form, many of the purest, most biologically dynamic (and therefore effective) nutrients are fresh-food-sourced. The hospital is a place where sick people go to get better...so why is it also the place where one of the most relevant paths toward that betterment is paved in excess refined sugars, sodium, saturated fats, bad cholesterol, simple/empty carbohydrates, and countless chemical poisons and preservatives that we can't even pronounce (let alone understand the long-term effects of as it's being swallowed)? Why is a facility built for and dedicated to healing the sick choosing to feed patients ingredients that are linked to the onset of diabetes, congestive heart failure, high blood pressure, and countless other nightmarish conditions...including *cancer*?! To put this another way: Why do hospitals feed their patients the foods that likely assisted in *putting them there in the first place*?

And I can't ignore this irony: Health supplements are so often banned from hospitals or individual patients because they are believed to conflict with the Western meds a patient has just been put on. So, a patient can't take supplements that were sourced from the soils of the earth, but they *can* be fed disease-causing ingredients nobody can pronounce. (Cue Serling's theme: *do-do-do-do...*)

Again: I appreciate the workers, and their precious labor, *so* much. People who make it their life goal to help others in need are true, Christ-like heroes to me. Bar none, they set the highest example of what we can do here on this planet while we wait for the Savior's return. But I will always have an issue with the fact that our hospitals—be it because of funding issues or otherwise—can't find a way to provide healthy nutrition to their patients, and while I *was* one of those patients, there was much on the menu I wasn't willing to put in my body.

With the food being as bad as it was, and my appetite and taste being what it was, I practically lived on cold, fruit-flavored gelatin. Of course, that is *not* a "heal and get your strength back" kind of diet (understatement of the century...). But between flavorlessness, nausea, and the dry-mouth sensation that made me feel as if I was trying to choke down desert sand from the most barren region of our planet's parched wastelands, I already couldn't bring myself to eat the high-carb, sugar-filled muffins and apple juice, let alone the full-plated, powdered-egg breakfast special with a side of mystery-preservative-sausage and bleached-flour white toast. If you don't eat at all, they'll never let you go home, so as sick as I was, gelatin was largely the only menu item I tolerated.

And, uhhh...yikes. Speaking of digestion problems: Just a couple days into my stay, unrelated to my abysmal diet, I had a very scary trip to the restroom that ultimately ended in the discovery of Clostridioides difficile in my stool. This bacterium, casually referred to as "C. diff" around a hospital, creates serious inflammation of the colon, *can* lead to certain colorectal cancers (according to developing sciences), and is said to be responsible for just under thirty thousand deaths annually in the United States alone. Abdominal pain, bloating, cramping, very dark and bloody "tar" stools, intense diarrhea throughout the day, and fevers are all common symptoms, but the most talked about feature of this gnarly germ is its infectiousness. It's *highly* contagious, as the spores "cling" to, and survive upon, surfaces for extended periods of time, and tend to float about...perhaps even literally.

Naturally, many readers' first question is how in the world I got this infection. I didn't have it when I was at home, and the symptoms started a day or two after I was moved from ICU and into the recovery room I would live in for weeks, so it was most likely contracted in that emergency room. But before readers assume it was due to unsanitary conditions of either the environment or the professionals' practice: Recent studies have looked at the possibility of aerial dissemination of C. diff spores (meaning it can be spread through the air) and, after discovering the presence of the bacterium high on the walls and in vents, have determined that's more than a mere possibility. I don't know how I got C. diff, or from where, but I can tell you that it is one of the worst infections you could ever come down with for a number of reasons.

Don't worry, I will spare you from going too far into detail, but suffice it to say that there is an odor, a color, and a consistency to the waste your body produces while infected with C. diff that would make any sane person in the universe want to deal with this in a comfortable and very *private* place, like home. Ideally, one *can* self-quarantine from home while recovering. (I would later learn the importance of restoring gut flora through the use of fermented foods and probiotics to be, in my opinion, a far superior and lasting way to recover from C. diff.) The last thing anyone would ever wish for is to have C. diff in a hospital—even if that person could walk on their own—as it requires: a) a whole additional, embarrassing layer of patient isolation and quarantining far away from all other people—a big rigamarole that the *entire floor of the hospital* has to be notified about; b) increased *Twilight Zone* "hovering hazmat space invaders" gear that the medical staff have to put on at the entrance of your room. These two dynamics are bad enough on their own. But, for those patients who *can't* walk, there is the humiliating bonus of diapers, and again without going into detail, trust me when I say a C. diff diaper-change is no ordinary diaper-changing experience. I'll leave it at that.

I had to be changed all throughout the day, and though these nurses and doctors kept it professional and compassionate (thank God!—bless their hearts!), I, as the woman who had to lay on that bed day in and day out for weeks on end, hated putting other human beings in the position to tend to such a personal and unpleasant infection. But I had no choice. There I was, like a baby stuck perpetually to a changing station, who just days prior would have been far too young, healthy, and agile to ever need another person to help with my bathroom needs, and now, suddenly, diapers *and* C. diff was my one-two punch from the boxing glove of reality. And what a wallop it was.

Then there was the unpleasant side effect of too many doctors—all certified to prescribe medicine, each claiming *their* medicines were the best, yet no two treatment plans were alike.

I did have a primary doctor (Dr. Bakir) as well as a primary oncologist (Dr. Ibrahim), and everyone on my floor was aware of that. However, as anyone who has stayed at the hospital for a while knows, you are subject to adjustments in your treatment as given by whatever additional doctors and specialists are on duty at the time. Almost daily (and that is no exaggeration), new faces in white lab coats came in, poked around, talked big words, and then placed me on new prescription drugs that were "necessary" for my recovery. Family members and patient advocates were not allowed to walk those floors, and I couldn't be my own health advocate. I was so weak that it was hard for me to have lengthy talks about what the new drug was, what it would do to me, and why it was necessary, and even when I spent my last drop of energy digging for answers, I never received a significant one. What I *did* receive was a confusing, lightning-fast, and wordy jumble delivered in a tone that sounded more like a sales pitch than a concerned practitioner's explanation of how this tweak in meds would benefit me.

I may not have always been the favorite patient of those nurses, but I frequently rejected new meds when dosing time came around, insisting that I must hear confirmation from Dr. Ibrahim before I start new protocols. When she did have a chance to swing by and check on me, I would tell her about the mysterious additions, she would pull them up in the network history, shake her head, and say, "I have no idea why they tried to put you on that. I'm cancelling that 'script. You don't need to take those."

The first several times that happened, I attempted to use the experience as a reason she should send me home so I wouldn't continue to be placed on dangerous meds I didn't need. I wanted to go home *so* bad… but it didn't work. She told me to hang in there and stay on the current course until I was well enough to go home responsibly, and meanwhile, she would check in frequently to help protect me from pointless pills. I want to say that I felt confident in each dose of mystery drugs that I rejected between her visits, but sometimes, in the back of my mind, the voice of doubt was prodding and poking: *What if that last medicine I just sent away was the one that would have made the difference in getting me out of here?*

A bit of a mind-game, it was…having so many doctors all swearing to be the one "in the know" over my situation. (Eventually, though, too many doctors spoiling the stew *would* be a factor in why, weeks later, Dr. Ibrahim would consent to my leaving, so I suppose there's a silver lining.) Yet perhaps the greater mind-game was the one I played with myself each time I saw my own withering, fading reflection.

I had never had a chance to properly accept the idea that I was dying of cancer in the first place. Now, after *one single* fainting spell, I was also temporarily paralyzed, in diapers, starving on flavorless gelatin, and separated from friends, family, and all familiar comforts with no end in sight, and the woman in the mirror was no longer the alligator-skin warrior I identified months earlier. Of all, this may have actually been the most intense *Twilight Zone* effect for those weeks. Each time I was given the opportunity to see what I was becoming, I was met with another wave of disbelief. It goes so far beyond superficial reports like, "I didn't look like myself." It wasn't just that I didn't resemble the person I used to be, it was that I didn't resemble a *person*, period. I looked like a villain plucked straight out of a sci-fi novel, or that stringy-haired Sméagol/Gollum guy from *Lord of the Rings* that crawls around mumbling to himself about "the precious." My buzz-cut hair was thicker in some patches and nearly bald in others. My skin was no longer that healthy mocha-brown, as it had been replaced with a pallor of ashen grey blended with a slight jaundice-yellow undertone—that is, when it wasn't also black and purple from the bruising that was now scattered all over my body (especially anywhere related to giving blood). The "whites" of my eyes were the color of a nicotine stain—sickening yellow bleeding in from the corners and blending near the middle so my "windows to the soul" painted a diseased landscape, indeed. My weight had plummeted to such a drastic degree that I could have beat Jack Skellington of *The Nightmare Before Christmas* in a skinny contest: just dark, purple/black/yellow/blue/grey skin draped like flesh-curtains over a stack of bones...and not just *any* bones: bones confined to a wheelchair and at the mercy of others to lift, move, carry, and put a fresh diaper on while nicotine-stained soul-windows stare back, blinking, unable to convey true gratitude since the woman behind them hasn't slept in weeks and could die at any moment. Without any help from Hollywood's special effects, makeup artists, or prosthetics, I could have walked into any audition and nailed the lead villain role...except, I imagine, that the viewers would later complain that my looks were too gruesome to be believable and they should have laid off a little.

It was bad. It was legitimately the hardest few weeks of my life. But the worst moment of all was when I found out I would *not* be home by Thanksgiving.

I couldn't believe it was happening. I really was just wasting away by the minute, and that update crushed me. I was devastated. By now, it was no surprise to anyone involved that I probably wasn't going to live very long, and that *this* Thanksgiving—a holiday marked by family gatherings and gratitude to be in good health and great company—would probably be my last, so why did they so firmly insist that I spend my final moments in this place? How could I have this kind of luck, spending Thanksgiving with a lengthy list of prescription drugs that no two doctors could agree I needed while the rest of the country was carving a turkey? I knew my husband and sister would help care for me if I could just get home. My sister was a nurse, for heaven's sake! And one who knew my medical history and background more intimately than any doctor or other medical professional could. John was strong, and my sons could be there, too, if needed… Why couldn't they just let me go home?

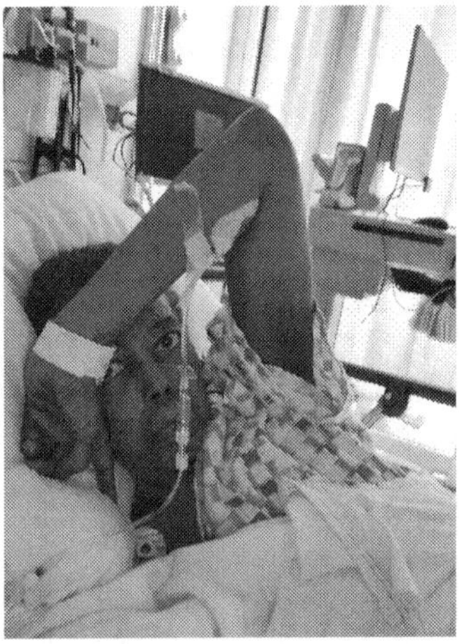

My face says it all: I wanted to go home, and I did *not* want my photo taken (thus my attempt to block my face with my arm)

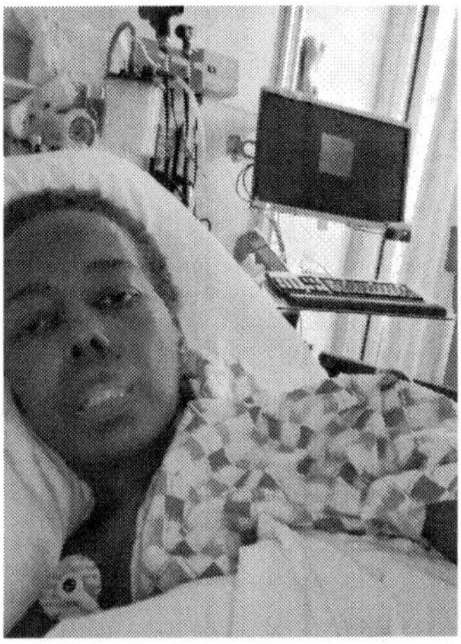

Thanksgiving Day, 2021—photo taken by a medical assistant on the worst holiday of my life

I hated it in that hospital. I will always be so grateful for those men and women who cared for me during that time—even if they did so in scary gear and behind muffling masks, and even when they tried to put me on unnecessary meds (well, for those whose motives were pure, that is). Always and forever, I will be thankful for every moment those people invested in my welfare. They, too, were missing out on their own family's turkey dinner so my sheets and diapers were clean. Oh, my goodness… Bless them for *that*!

But I cannot explain to you readers just how desperately I dreamed of home every moment of every day, and just how *slow* time moved in a place that felt like a prison sentence where you *also* cannot sleep through any of those seconds, minutes, or hours that drag...on...forever. Until you've personally lived it, you just can't understand the anguish of being told you've got very little time left on this earth and, simultaneously, being told you have to spend it in a *Twilight Zone* episode. It's like you're hearing, "Hurry up and live while you still can!" at the same time as, "Whoa! Slow down...recovery is gonna take a while."

One small, tender mercy from the Father was the gift of the window in my room. Had I been placed in the middle of the cluster of patient rooms on my floor, I wouldn't have had a window to look through. It may not sound like much to others, but trust me, when you are completely cut off from the rest of the outside world and the people you are in contact with always approach you as though you might infect them, God's beautiful morning sky, and His mysterious nighttime sky, is a real escape.

And this same small, tender mercy from God was my sole companion on Thanksgiving Day, 2021. Well, the window *and* my thoughts. Yeah... those were there, too. Oh, and my Thanksgiving dinner: a few teaspoons of strawberry Jell-O.

The Bible had a character who could identify with my situation, even though the circumstances were different. His name was *Job*, and throughout the holidays, I contemplated him often. He had lost everything overnight, including his home, all of his children, and his health. At the end of his rope—when he, too, had no true companion except the boils and blisters that itched so tremendously he had to use the sharp edges of broken pottery to relieve the itch—his faith in God never wavered. He certainly had his own why-God-why moments as any of us would, but in the end, when *his* "Thanksgiving dinner" was threatened, Job held steadfast and true to the Almighty Creator of the universe.

And so would I. No matter what. He was my God, my personal Savior, who already redeemed me from a fate worse than death—*a fate worse than this*—and if there was ever a time I needed reminded of that, it was now. I might have physically been on that hospital bed, but in light of eternity, I had already been saved.

Heavenly perspective, Lynette...heavenly perspective.

It took a lot of self-counseling to keep from losing my mind in those final days in the hospital, especially when Dr. Ibrahim came in to give me the sad update: My body, despite all the chemotherapy I had taken to kill off the cancer cells, was still being eaten alive. My scans still looked to be a giant blur of black blobs. She certainly *tried* to encourage me…and it was so sweet, hearing her words—statements like, "You're going to be okay," or, "I can't wait to see what you do with your life," and other thoughtful, yet compassionately vague sentiments—but there was no pulling out of her any specific good news regarding my survival. I had the impenetrable "stage four." That terminal, fatal, incurable, inoperable, ready-or-not, here-it-comes breast cancer. And as uplifting as Dr. Ibrahim wanted to be, she also never lied…

…So, as it turned out, I was still dying. Despite Cislyn's words—or, rather, God's words *through* Cislyn—Chemo and Cancer were still battling it out, and Chemo looked like he was losing.

Fearful Lynette was enjoying her buffet of doubts and worry. I had to try harder than ever to silence her now that the Cislyn promise of a "touch" didn't look as likely as it had the day she first said it. But even though every single sign pointed to imminent death and I couldn't get my doctor to say anything to the contrary, *God* had said I would live.

Therefore, I would live. It was that simple.

Feast on that, Fearful Lynette.

After all, God already brought me back once. Clearly, He wanted me here for some grand purpose and, like Job, I would always be willing to live out that purpose. All that was left to do now was figure out what that calling looked like. But I *would* live.

Right God…?

Yeah. I would live. I just had to figure out how. What I was currently doing wasn't working. Yet God had made Himself clear. How could I do the "living" thing God promised if *all this chemo-hell later I'm still dying as fast as before?*

It gave me something to think about, anyway. It's probably good that it did, because when I got home, I was a lot more receptive to switching things around.

Between Thanksgiving and the day I finally left to go home, I had been given a short but crucially important list of things the doctors wanted to see before I would be discharged: 1) stable vitals; 2) at least a few uninterrupted steps on my own with a walker; and 3) PICC-line installed. For many days now, my vitals looked satisfactory, and though it hurt like the dickens, I applied myself to physical therapy with grit, pushing through the pain day in and day out, until I could finally, with my walker, take a step or two on my own. (Therapy was nowhere *near* over, but it was satisfactory enough for me to carry on from home.) That took care of the first two items for now. A PICC (peripherally inserted central catheter) line is installed on the inside of the upper arm for fluids, medications, and liquid nutrition. I wasn't eating, so I would have no choice but to live off of intravenous nutrition bags, and though it certainly did make blood draws and medicines easier, the location of the PICC was incredibly uncomfortable. I couldn't let my arm rest normally, and sleeping on my side was entirely out of the question. It was this awkward, plastic, sharp, pokey thing worming its way through a vein that travels directly to the heart. To put it simply, you *cannot* tug on that setup…so I just had to hold my arm out in a cumbersome position for weeks on end. In the beginning, I was on that liquid nutrition for *eighteen hours per day*—a part of my treatment I will always remember as agonizing…laying there, holding my arm in funky positions for over twice as long as a person's average workday. Yeesh.

(When we got home, there was quite a bit of drama associated with the line when the nurses who came to my house forgot a critical step during blood draws. Well before blood is stored in a vial from a PICC line, the nurse is supposed to pull back ten milliliters of fluid and discard it so the blood doesn't get confused with the liquid in the line. Then, the second draw is considered to be a viable sample. When the nurses came to my house to follow up with me, they forgot this first step and submitted the fluid in the line as a blood sample. Thankfully, this error was discovered and rectified, because otherwise I might have been carted off to the infusion center and given medications I didn't need when the labs mistook the line-fluid as my blood. After it happened a second time, my oncologist said it would be best if I just came into the lab in person to have blood drawn.)

But *at least* I was home, in my own bed, where John, Laura, and the rest of my family let me get the rest I needed whenever I needed it. They had so recently been told they would never see me again, so, although all of our hearts were filled to the brim with joy when I was discharged, there wouldn't be a grand welcoming party. For my own good (and boy did I appreciate it!), my homecoming was anticlimactic: carried out on the hush-hush down-low, quickly but carefully, while John insisted that everyone give me plenty of space and avoid visiting the house for a while. I hardly remember much from those first few days home other than sleeping, but far from being hurt or offended that there wasn't a giant love-fest upon my arrival home, the greatest gift anyone could have given me beyond the few gentle hugs I received was space and rest.

Laura and John could see the difference in me as well. Laura, as a nurse, sees sickness and death related conditions all the time, and when she saw my distended belly, jaundice-colored eyes, sunken-back cheeks, protruding bones all over, and my burn-victim chemo-skin, she started planning my funeral.

Home really is where the heart is, even in the most tumultuous seasons of life. It's a place of comfort, where I can hear the familiar voice of John and Laura right outside the door instead of strangers, even when the subject of their conversation is still related to my sickness, symptoms, and treatment. Home is where so many prayer warrior friends of mine dropped off organic, homemade foods to help us out, and if I was feeling up for a visit that day, they would come and pray with me. Home is where I can fall asleep and stay asleep for more than a twenty-minute interval, allowing my beyond-weary and completely atrophied muscles to sink into a mattress that was actually designed for *sleep* (as opposed to the mattresses at the hospital that are designed for a one-night stay but feel like they're clandestine weapons of torture). Home is where Ann brought soup and grocery gift cards, Christine brought fellow-cancer-patient camaraderie, Curtis and Vivian brought the most incredible homemade bread...ah, I could not wait to be back!

And just to bring the *Twilight Zone* comparison to a contrasting close: Home is a place where people wear normal clothing, not hazmat suits, and their facial features are uncovered—free to express real feelings and reaction; where a person can reach out and grab your hand without everyone in the vicinity gasping and jerking away in fear of a potential COVID-19 germ; where food ingredients are healthy and fresh, and nobody will ever be forced to choke down solidified-liquid sugar-gelatins that jiggle more than they nourish; where cords are looped and stored in a drawer instead of hooked up all over your body; where lights go out and *stay* out when the switch on the wall is pointing down, instead of blinking all night long in every direction; where repetitious sounds, loud beeping, and annoying heart monitors that malfunction are all traded for silence or the occasional worship song or hymn; where I never need question the motives of the person coming through the door or fear their next unnecessary prescription; where quarantine, isolation, and severe loneliness is replaced with the presence of family and the occasional, John-approved visitor who knows and loves me more intimately than the closest doctor or nurse at any hospital ever could.

Where I felt *just a little* less like a female Job than I did in the weeks prior.

I was *so* happy to be in this elusive, magical place called "home," even though my recovery would have some rough times ahead, like the painful bedsore that developed on my buttock due to lack of blood supply to the skin in the area, or the many C.-diff-infected diapers my husband had to change for me. (My unbelievable, considerate husband got more than he bargained for in taking care of *that*. Poor guy. It was more than just embarrassing, as I never imagined I would be in a position to rely on him so helplessly and vulnerably, but he took "for better or worse; through sickness and health" seriously the day he married me. Praise the Lord for men like John...and for sisters like Laura!) Throughout the series of tough days, however, I was finally about to experience the return of some of the strength I had lost during the past year, both emotional and physical. God had something *major* planned for my future and my body. All I had to do was be still and quiet, know that He is God, and keep my spiritual eyes and ears open so I could recognize the epiphany for what it was the minute He revealed it.

And that time was coming sooner rather than later. The directives from God that would change my life—and allow me to touch the lives of countless others from that day on—were waiting to be discovered within the next few steps...

Literally the next few steps.

Chapter Fifteen

BEATING THE STEPS

Up to this point, Readers, I have intentionally let the dismal part of my testimony breathe, without rushing through any of it. I did this intentionally because, even though I would normally want to get past the crud more quickly so I can spend more time giving glory to God, I can't expect anyone to completely grasp and soak in the amazing *healing* portion of my journey without first "feeling the horror alongside me." So, I took the necessary time to think about and share every side effect, every moment of pain, every general hurt caused by both the disease, and the medicine, that God never made. My story is no different from so many other people out there who have suffered immensely when they very likely didn't have to.

Were you able to trek along? Did you wipe away a tear or two? Scrunch up your nose or furrow your brow? Have I had you on the hook this entire book long waiting to see just how I was ever, *ever* going to come back from such an irreversibly dead place?

I hope so, because if that is the case, then the juxtaposition you will now experience through my testimony will sing a little louder. We have now officially reached that moment in my story where things begin to permanently shift toward my miracle, based on the plants of the soil that *God* made, *not* chemotherapy. It started first by doing whatever I had to do to reverse the damage to my legs, and through a *crucial* bit of power reclaimed in that experience, I finally had the strength and bravery I needed to unplug *from the Western machine...*

After I had been home for a day or two, a petite-built, young, Asian physical therapist began coming to my house for regular visits. She was a friendly gal, at times making small talk about her husband and children, though she didn't linger long on any topic unrelated to my progress.

At times, she was incredibly firm, which surprised me. Sure, she was tiny, but she was also good at her job and could be quite the drill sergeant, effectively knowing just how hard and how far to push to help patients overcome their own physical or mental limitations. And actually, that slightly impersonal and militant approach to treatment could be appreciated because my health insurance had approved six weeks of physical therapy, with two sessions per week included in this protocol, and the therapist was not willing to waste one moment of our limited time together.

She and I had one mutual goal: to get me walking again...but that meant something very different to each of us, as the following days would show.

Our exercises started with what sounded like the simplest goal: I needed to begin to put weight on my feet again. Although I *had* taken a few weak steps in the hospital, at that time, it was for the purpose of proving I could get to and from the bathroom to fulfill the minimum requirements of discharge. On my end, it had nothing to do with "walking again." The price tag on my ticket home said "a few steps," so I was going to pay three steps, the bare minimal just to get what I wanted and get out of there; anything beyond that could be worried about some other day.

Now, here we were: That "some other day" had arrived, and I was confronted with having to identify what the goal truly was *for myself*, regardless of what that may have meant for my care team.

Remember that, according to the Western medical narrative, I was still "incurable" with only "months" to live several months prior—meaning I was already supposed to be gone by now and was living on weeks of borrowed time already—so their goal for my physical therapy was... what, exactly? Walking on my own two feet into the next memorial supplies shop and picking out my own headstone? Sure, I know that's a bit cynical, but it just seemed strange to me that patients who are actively dying and already miserable would be asked to spend their *final* moments on earth facing unthinkable pins-and-needles neuropathy pain in therapy appointments, instead of just being allowed to rest in wheelchairs and make lasting memories with the family members who remain. If I dug around for answers, I'm sure I would find many valid, "quality of life" reasons to justify coaching patients to participate in these goals so late in their lives, but those reasons wouldn't have mattered much to me at the time. I was exhausted, mentally and physically, and what little energy I had left needed to be spent on the essentials for my personal situation: I didn't need to know why *everyone else* believed this therapy was a good idea for terminal patients; I needed to know how *I* felt about it before I could even begin to apply myself to goals that required me to experience pain I didn't want and consume strength I didn't have.

Was I in this because the care team had a box to check and it was my responsibility as a smiley, cooperative patient to go along with it? Or was I in this because I, Lynette Hill, wanted to walk again? If the former, physical therapy would be easy enough. I would just push my feet against a couple foam blocks or something, make a bunch of grunting sounds, and play the "sorry it didn't work out but thanks for trying" card. If the latter, it would have to mean so much more to me than increasing my quality of life until my inevitable death, because I would *not* spend six weeks putting myself through hell just so I could get one or two good weeks of walking in before I left this body and went to be with God.

If *I*, Lynette Hill, really applied myself to physical therapy, it would be because my "imminent and inevitable death" was off the table entirely. It would mean that I had officially and fervently rejected the "months to live" prognosis handed to me by mankind's medicine and chosen instead to believe God was going to raise me up into a long and fruitful future. Certainly, that would make all the difference in the world when it came to how I was about to handle the pain that was yet ahead of me…so it was crucial that I proceed knowing just how sure I was in my belief that God was going to bring me out of this. I could say it with my lips, and *I had*—"God said He was *going to* touch me, and that's all there is to it!"—but did I *really* believe that? Completely and entirely? Down to the heart and soul? Without question?

Did I?

The next few days—and the next few steps—were going to put that to the test, try my metals again, and force me to know who I truly am as one whose real name is "Daughter of the King." I was about to prove to myself that I was not the frilly, girly, spoiled princess asking her heavenly Daddy for a credit card and an easy out. As a daughter of the King of the universe, I *was* a princess, but I was of the warrior build: one who could push through and survive *anything*...and then end up all the stronger for it where the world expected nothing less than my complete annihilation. I was about to shock a lot of people...

It would be so much more than physical therapy. What I was about to learn would push me into new levels of radical reliance on God, as well as confidence in myself as an individual with thoughts and opinions of my own that would, in at least one critical area, fundamentally and diametrically go against society's narrative regarding medicine. It was true that I was now embarking upon the very last stretch of my cancer journey, but unbeknownst to doctors, cancer experts, and even family, the "last stretch" for me wouldn't actually be "the last" of anything.

It would be the beginning of everything.

And it would all start with putting weight on my feet.

It was still horrifically painful to place my feet flat on the ground, as the neuropathy that had settled into those tissues made for nearly unbearable pain conditions. Every time I made contact with the floor, the sensation was a torturous eruption of pins and needles. Then, adding my body weight to the equation—something that the physical therapist called "weight-bearing exercises"—brought on additional layers of stinging, agonizing pain.

To assist with holding me upright and steady, the therapist would stand behind me wearing a belt-type device with a large loop dangling from each of her hips that came up and encircled my midsection. Then, as I attempted forward steps with my walker, my weight was further supported by her. Despite how small this woman was, she was at least a thousand times stronger than me in those moments, and my attachment to her would restrain me from falling if or when my legs proved untrustworthy. After attempting five steps, she would allow me to sit, where I would face a series of leg-lifts from different angles.

One day—a day that *began* like any other but ended with a promise of something new—I was in the midst of trying to slowly transfer my body weight to my own standing capacity, and the pain was so unbearable that all I could do was wobble pathetically and cry. The goal was no more than the usual five steps, but I was just so tired of *pain, pain, all-the-time pain and sickness* that I was struggling emotionally as well as in body. My therapist, young as she may have been, was perceptive and experienced enough in this line of work that she could see the crossroad I was parked at: I was either going to fail forever or get my life back, and much of that outcome would be based on whatever move I made next. Whether she saw it quite that transparently or not, she did recognize my hesitation and took that opportunity to explain to me that the only way to overcome the horrors of this condition was to retrain my body how to move, despite the agony that came alongside this journey. If I didn't find, harness, and ride a deep drive within me to run this race against myself and *win*, I could remain atrophied and on pain medications for the rest of my life. This woman picked up on the fragility and importance of that moment and, in the interest of challenging me to get past it in the right direction, nailed me with a dire warning.

"If you don't put your foot down and take a step, you will be in a wheelchair forever. Is that what you want?"

I nearly winced at the suggestion. Choosing a wheelchair for life if it wasn't necessary? Who would ever want that?

"No," she answered for me. "I didn't think so. Now *push through...*"

Push through...

The words resonated within me. I was standing at the precipice of failure or greatness, and an entire future of physical freedom loomed ahead of me—walking, leaping, spinning, dancing, running, jogging—everything I had ever done with my legs before and could imagine ever doing in the days ahead. And she was right. The choice was mine to make. And folks, I can't emphasize this enough: the energy needed from me to make this happen? I didn't have it. I really *did not* have it. I was so weak and tired. I'm telling you that the strength you're about to read about was supernatural. But if I continued to wallow and cry and think about the pain, I would be tempting fate, asking for the neuropathy and nerve damage that this cancer had already pummeled me with to be permanent. But if that wasn't the future I wanted—if I wanted to take ownership over my own life, slap cancer in the face for daring to think it could mess with me, and store up a treasure trove of physical liberty in the *years* I believed were yet to come—then I had to take that painful, pins-and-needles step...and take it like a boss.

Push through!

I steadied my gaze, focused on an area further back in my living room, clenched my jaw in determination, and curled my knuckles around that walker with the ferocity of a lion devouring its prey. I *could* do this—no,

I *had to* do this. God had said I was going to live, and that meant more than merely avoiding death; it meant I was going to *soar*.

Starting now…

There it is, Faithful Lynette said, awakening within me and stirring excitedly. *You feel that, Lynette? That deep, intense fight beginning to prick your senses? Do you feel the way you're clenching your jaw, clamping those knuckles, releasing the anxiety through the breath of your lips? You feel that anger rising up within you at the very thought that cancer would own even ONE MORE piece of your life?!*

Yeah…I felt it. Though the strong woman in me had taken quite a beating and fallen asleep for a time, I could feel her fury pulsating. The warrior. The giant. The alligator-skinned princess within me. I could feel her arising alright, and she was *mad*.

Good, good, Faithful Lynnette goaded on. *Let it feed you. Let it drive you. You smell that freedom? Can you taste that future, out wrestling Neo in the sunshine again without a worry or care for doctors, medications, or blobs on scans?*

My feet screamed in pain as one pound of body weight after another transferred to them. I had managed to come to a full stance. Now I just had to walk for five steps.

Don't you dare falter. Don't do it, Lynette. Let that righteous anger you feel over the life this disease tried to steal from you push you to take it back! Come on! Take it back! You're finished with this whole cancer business—done being owned by death—and you know it, don't you?

Faithful Lynette was laughing aloud in my heart. Though nothing had yet happened, because Faithful Lynette is the deepest part of me, she was laughing in advance about the triumph that was coming.

Hahaha! You're done being owned by death! Ha! You know it, don't you!?

God was incrementally revealing to me a path toward healing and I was determined to follow it. In the next few days and weeks, God would open my eyes to astounding truths and sciences about the relationship between cancer and the human body, but in this moment, He only required one thing from me: take a step.

I just didn't know how big of a deal a single step would be or what it could represent…but He did.

Through the tears, I began to press harder, forcing myself to shove my feet into the invisible razor blades that had become my floor. On the outside, I may have had a blubbery face, and I may have been releasing a few short, whimpering sobs, but on the inside, the warrior was saddling her horse and pulling her awesome dreadlocks into a braid so it wouldn't get in the way of what she was about to do…

The last time a season of my life could appropriately fit a theme song, it was *The Twilight Zone*. But on this day, in my living room, listening to my strong inner voice and talking myself through what felt like a mile-long barefoot journey over a sea of glass, it was almost as if those powerful, punchy, adrenaline-infused synth-hits at the beginning of *Eye of the Tiger* had popped into the atmosphere.

Except I wasn't Rocky Balboa. I was a force perhaps even steelier than he, and now that Alligator-Lynette was sharpening her blade, my enemy, Cancer, had a new challenger…and it wasn't Chemo. To the strong Lynette who refused to lay down on the tracks and die, the fight was nothing to be afraid of. In fact, it was nothing less than the purest thrill, so long as the glory of the inevitable victory could be God's. Rising up to the challenge of her rival, Cancer, Lynette was about to burst through the wall of pain with a roar!

Go, go, go! Press in and push through! Remember the time Cancer stole your movie night with John and sent your entire life into a spiral from that moment forward?

Yes. I remembered that. And as I inched forward, unseen needles now pricking up beyond the ankles, I blinked the tears from my eyes and bore down into another step.

That's it, Lynette! Keep going… Remember when you saw Cancer crawling through your tissues for the first time and it was just blobs everywhere? So much disease and destruction throughout your body that you couldn't even tell where his cells ended and yours began on the scans? Does it make you mad, thinking back?

Yes. I remembered that, too. Yes, it made me furious! I was done being stolen from. And as I shoved my heel into the red, hot coals pretending to be my living room carpet, ignoring the beads of sweat as they trickled down the back of my neck, I released an enormous gust of anxious breath…and pressed further in.

The warrior within me pulled her breastplate on snug, cinched her boots, and slipped her arm into the grip of her shield, releasing a fearless laugh that would carry on the wind to Cancer's hideout. He was done for, and she *finally* believed it, heart and soul.

Remember when you went in for a "routine checkup" and Cancer nearly killed you, successfully robbing you and your family of Thanksgiving?

Yes! I remembered it! All of it! I would never forget! And as I picked up my blistering, useless foot from behind me, I eased it out in front, pushing it deliberately into the invisible grenade and enduring the ensuing explosion. The pain nearly made me pass out, but I steadied myself and proceeded into the final step.

Are you ready, here and now, to take God's promise of life and healing and own it?

Yes, I was ready.

Will you do whatever you have to do to receive that blessed, blood-bought miracle God promised you?

Yes, I was willing to push through it all.

Are you finished letting Cancer steal from you? Your health, your body, your home, your family, and your life...? Are you done?

Yes. I was finished.

For real this time.

Cancer would never own me again. And I had just taken the steps to prove that.

The warrior in me, usually buried deep under tiers of timidity, was in charge now. Cancer may not have been completely gone in that moment, but I *was* a strong and powerful woman, as God designed me to be, and those five steps I took in physical therapy was the beginning of the end for my disease. I was finished being owned, being robbed, and though the victory was only over a battle, and not the big-picture war, I had just won...and something about it tasted too good not to partake of again at my soonest opportunity.

Victory was God's...and it would continue to be so, as He said.

"Well done," my physical therapist offered with a proud smile.

"Thanks," I panted, lowering myself down into a sitting position. This young therapist had absolutely no idea what just occurred in my living room, but it was a heck of a lot more than five steps worth of progress.

I was going to win this.

Chapter Sixteen

WESTERN VS. NATURAL—ROUND TWO

When my physical therapy was over that one victorious day, I felt both triumphant and exhausted. During these long days, outside of the appointments with my young, drill-sergeant friend, I found myself with a lot of time to sit and reflect on my situation. I kept thinking back to the strange ambiance of the hospital setting, and I couldn't help but feel more and more keenly aware of the connection between horrific symptoms and chemotherapy. It was really no secret that chemotherapy is *brutal* on the human body (even my oncologist had used that exact word to describe it), and the longer I was separated from that hospital, the more the flashback memories of me swallowing those pills felt like I had been a part of some dark poison factory.

"Poison factory." The words sound conspiratorial, as if the only people who would call it that are those silly folks with anti-mindreading homemade tinfoil hats who spend their evenings telescoping for UFOs and assigning illuminati labels to everyone in politics. Regardless of how melodramatic one might accuse me of being for using those words, though, I'm certainly not the only one to make that connection. In the next few weeks of my life, when the ball really got rolling on my personal research online, I would find that the word "poison" is not only frequently associated with chemotherapy and its effects upon the human body, it's quite literally common knowledge even among Western medical and scientific authorities who perpetuate and champion the use of it. Though they prefer to assign it a less offensive name—"chemotherapy toxicity" (which means the exact same thing in my opinion)—their own articles often go as far as to use the very word "poison."

Just to toss out a quick example, our very own National Institute of

Health openly acknowledges "most chemotherapy medications have a *poisonous* effect on the body's cells."[1] Another source doesn't even try to candy-coat the truth in syrupy language. Using the term even more directly—ironically in an article titled "Chemotherapy is Poison; No, Literally" (wow; tell us how you *really* feel!)—is the Illinois Science Council, flatly stating, "all chemotherapies *are poisons*: they are chemicals that kill cells."[2] Other sources acknowledge that chemotherapy is a poison, but they drape ambiguous synonyms around it so they don't have to be the medical community's official antagonist who called the kettle black. The American Cancer Society is one such source. Instead of using the word "poison," they use the very *definition of* poison to describe chemotherapy, saying: "Chemotherapy drugs are considered to be hazardous to people who handle them or come into contact with them"[3] (i.e., uhhh...maybe don't put that in your body?).

Flashes of memories were haunting me, pinpricking my mind invasively until it was almost all I could think about: Me, nearly dead, masked nurses hovering over me, calling me "Mrs. Hill" instead of Lynette, and a tablet of poison heading toward my lips... Why did I so suddenly feel like I needed to leap into my own flashback and smack that thing away from my mouth before I swallowed it? When did my internal sensors go from thinking of this as "harsh but necessary medicine" to some kind of...euthanasia?

I was still taking it every day by this point, but it had started to feel wrong.

Sinful, almost.

It was getting harder as the minutes passed to put "chemo" in the same sentence as "benefits" and still render a statement that made sense to me; in fact, putting extreme toxins in an immunocompromised body and labeling it "therapy" had long since sounded absurd...now it was just comical.

All day, any day, I have no problem at all saying and truly believing that the doctors, nurses, and medical assistants who administer chemotherapy—both inside and outside of the hospital—are doing so with pure and loving motives. It wasn't *them* that I questioned as much as it was the Western system. Even outside of cancer, the Western medical system has far more than earned itself some scrutiny, and it was not as much directed toward the doctors and nurses, but to their training.

How is it that not one single professional up to this point—*not one!*—asked me about my diet and what good or bad things I might be putting in my body on a daily basis? There was a day when a physician would have started with that, and *every relevant approach to the treatment from that point forward would have flowed from that foundation*...but now, it's not even a question on the radar?!

Something was very wrong here, and though it hadn't occurred to me to be too offended about it before, suddenly, I couldn't shake how downright preposterous this all was. What started as a casual pondering began to grow; within a couple of days, this question about diet, and many others like it, had drilled holes into my peace until I found myself looping about why such key topics in medicine had become obscure or hidden away. Wasn't it *so* obvious to ask a dying person what they had been eating, drinking, applying to their skin, spraying in their hair, inhaling at the factory, and other such exposures? For all the system knew, I was eating breast-cancer-causing pesticides on the surface of my vegetables up to ten times per day, and the first layer of cancer treatment could have been as simple as switching to organic produce! But the Western medical system doesn't train its professionals to even *think* about that.

Setting aside for a moment the sweet and sincere motives of the *people* who participate within it, the Western medical system itself responds to sickness largely by: a) bypassing the underlying condition or cause of the condition and focusing only on relieving the symptoms; b) consulting the charts, lists, or networks to see what lab-produced medication relieves those symptoms; c) only *sometimes* catching all the side effects that this lab-produced medication might further cause the patient down the road; all while d) *almost never* consulting any naturopathic or holistic research to see if a plant-based response (or an elimination of bad habits) might have been the fastest, *gentlest* cure! It's a one-treatment-fits-all approach to sickness that likewise assumes all ailments in all body types are going to respond equally to any given drug: Symptom A is relieved by Drug B, which equals Recovery Plan C. Boom, done. (Oh, yeah, and now the patient pays Hefty Medical Bill D...)

At some point, almost everyone has been drawn into a conversation on this topic, or watched a quick video, etc., that raises issues regarding the trustworthiness of the Western medical system. And just as often, someone makes comments suggesting that the entire structure is set up to intentionally make people sick so Big Pharma can cash in on the most vulnerable in society. Though I'm not so sure that's my own personal take on what's happening, I mentioned this familiar sentiment to illustrate that we do see *some* level of widespread societal distrust in Western medicine.

But, people are so busy these days trying to keep up with the speed of the Western world (half of which is now run by electronics—good luck competing with *that* speed, fellow humans…), that we don't have time to research proper healing for ourselves, so we remain ignorant about our own healing until we end up sick. Then, in a vulnerable place—scared, sick, in pain, and in a hurry for *any* relief we can get as fast as we can get it—we rush back to the Western doctors and ask them for drugs. Within just a few generations of this, Gramma's home remedies are gone, forever replaced by harsh, but fast-acting, pharmaceuticals. Even the occasional doctors who *have* self-educated beyond the Western prescriptions list are often not taken seriously by their patients if they dare suggest a safer, more natural treatment that takes a couple weeks or doesn't alleviate symptoms immediately. Patients are so used to viewing doctors as rapid-response-drug vending machines now that the Western system has no motive to slow down and repair its own shortcomings.

And let's not forget the number of patients who wouldn't heed the more natural methods anyway, regardless of their efficacy and simplicity… Everyone knows that one guy who, if the doctor said, "Bob, you have *got* to lay off beer and pizza or your diabetes is gonna kill you!" his response would be, "You got it, Doc!" followed by a drive straight to the nearest full-bar-and-buffet joint as soon as the appointment is over. At the *next* appointment, Bob's insulin prescription dosage is increased… right alongside his pizza and beer intake. So, to some degree, the broken, quick-drugging, over-medicated, and nutritionally under-trained Western system has been built upon the laziness of its own consumers. (Not everything is a big conspiracy, folks. Sometimes, "Bob" *does* have a role to play in his own health whether he likes it or not!)

Regardless of all these details, though, *my* story wasn't Bob's. *I* didn't live on beer and pizza; *I* lived on vegetarian dishes rich in vitamins and nutrients, and I had done so for going on three decades. These doctors may corporately feel a quick prescription drug is appropriate for those patients whose lives actually will be lengthened by pharmaceutical intervention because they lack the self-motivation and drive necessary to put in the work toward natural healing, but none of that needed to apply to *me.*

It just bugged me: Why hadn't even one doctor asked me the most rudimentary question regarding my diet? Why—or, *why with me*—did they calculate that Symptom A would be relieved by Drug B, and then just slap me with Recovery Plan C?

And, come to think of it…could it be that pesticides on my vegetables for every meal actually played a bigger role in my cancer than I had thought?

Honestly—that had probably done it. At the very least, it didn't help.

All these considerations I had never put much thought into… Now that I was away from the hospital, at home, with a lot of time on my hands, and at least rested enough that my brain could parse these rudimentary concepts, the standard approach to medicine was just pricking my spirit a bit. I could feel God off to the side, waving red flags and trying to get my attention, but every time I thought I turned His direction, a cloud moved in and obscured me from seeing His warnings for what they were. It was clear He wanted me to keep praying and seeking Him in this area, and that was something I had all the time in the world to do now.

One particular contemplation kept floating through my mind on repeat. At first, it lingered in the peripheral of my thoughts, but it eventually became such a needling idea that it moved to the front and center, demanding stronger consideration, and I finally had to address it: I had known and believed that God was going to heal me because of what He said through Cislyn, but now, the all-natural way Cislyn had survived cancer decades back kept floating through my mind: It wasn't a big pharmaceutical intervention, a million appointments with "blob scans," or through many seasons of mouth sores, scaley skin, nausea, vomiting, and missing out on her family holidays. She just went *organic and clean*, as simple as that, leaving the details about cancer cells to God and the wind. It's true that she had originally said she might still have cancer as far as anyone knew, and, in the beginning, that really bothered me. But, when I looked at her—the way she talked, walked, prayed, conversed…the way she *lived!*—I didn't see "cancer." I saw "life." I, too, wanted to do more than just "survive." I wanted to *thrive*, and Cislyn managed it by planting a garden and only putting into her body the plants that God, Himself, grew. If there was a single cancer cell still floating around in Cislyn's body somewhere, nobody was any the wiser…

Meanwhile, look at her go, Lynette. Hmmm…

Was a new day dawning for me right here, right now, in this moment? Was God's Spirit revealing to me that His plan for healing might actually be as radical as Cislyn's?

God, is that what You're trying to tell me? Faithful Lynette asked. *Could it be that this entire Western response to cancer—a sickness You never made in Your Creation to begin with—is something I should…* (I dared not even think it at first.) *Something I should discontinue?*

Don't be foolish, Fearful Lynette responded. *Take your pills before you keel over!*

Wow. If I ever needed prayerful direction from God, it was now. There was no doubt about it: I had officially begun a journey toward answers, and prayer would be the way I would begin.

Immediately.

I prayed for God to show me a path toward the abundant life that He promises in His word (John 10:10). As an investment in my own health, sometimes I did the leg lifts shown to me by the physical therapist in between session in addition to giving a hundred percent of my efforts during the sessions.

I really had felt the strongest version of myself pull through in that therapy visit, when the needling pain of neuropathy in my feet was so bad it was like knives biting into the flesh with each step, but I had *done it anyway*, conquering fear and pain in the meantime. I also knew that was just the beginning, and I was committed to keeping the new, warrior-Lynette standard. That would prove to be very necessary in the days to come. I was *going to* beat this, but I was still weak.

During the preceding months, my illness had ravaged my body and tormented my mind. When I looked in the mirror, I saw remnants of a woman I had once been. The previously thriving facial features had diminished, traded for a worn and skeletal frame, from within which sunken eyes peered out. My naked, exposed scalp which once featured those long, lovely dreadlocks, now showed the contours of the weary and worn skull which so badly needed to know true rest.

I had been rendered nearly helpless, with my husband and sister caring for me full time. The nutrition my body received was taken in through an intravenous bag that I remained connected to for eighteen hours a day. My body had been given bagged nutrients and other food-substitutes for long enough that mustering the energy to eat food was challenging at times. I was thankful to be alive, of course, but I was after more than just survival now.

During this time, time itself was, once again, an enigma. Some days raced by, while others seemed eternal. Though I had willed my mind into a positive place, it was a constant fight to keep it there, so I increased some good habits, like playing Gospel music or ocean sounds during my times of rest. I started wondering if there were any other options out there that we could be missing in our search for effective treatments, since planting a garden and eating homegrown veggies seemed too little and too late at this stage in my illness. And, it occurred to me, I happened to have a lot of time on my hands to look for answers since I was stuck in that chair, tied down to my IV "food."

I had conquered the thinking part. Now it was time to dig.

Figuring I may as well spend the time fruitfully on this new journey, I started reading online, looking for something that might make a difference for my health. My pursuit began with an online search engine and the phrase "natural cures for cancer."

Ambitious, I know…but I was on a warrior's high, and having dominated those five steps (and more since), no idea was too grand for me to consider a possibility.

As I began to search, I was amazed by the sheer volumes of treatments discussed within natural realms of health that were never mentioned by conventional doctors. Evidently, there was healing for almost every malady in human history, all from the soil (even if in concentrated forms, like supplements), including cancer, but certainly not limited to cancer. And, instead of viewing the growing list with the skeptical lens I may have once peered through, my recent hours in prayer to the Maker of that soil encouraged me to approach this subject with an open mind.

One of the first natural cancer treatments I read about was that of turkey tail mushrooms. I watched a video wherein a man stood, giving a testimonial about his own mother's health. The cancer portion of his narrative was all too familiar to me: this woman, according to doctors, was suffering terminally, her condition was beyond help, and the cancer was so far advanced that her treatment had shifted to prioritizing her comfort until the end, as opposed to focusing on her cure.

Sounded familiar…a little too painfully familiar, actually.

But that also wasn't the end of the story for these folks.

From a diagnosis of doom, to finding a path of hope and healing, this man and his mother had lived the testimony I wanted for myself. At the end of the video, the man brought his mother—who was still living and claimed to be cancer-free—up onto the stage with him to celebrate *five years* of post-cancer health!

Huh… I thought to myself. *Coincidence? A fluke, maybe? I have no reason to think they're lying, but if a few mushrooms could cure cancer, wouldn't everyone be cured by now?*

Wary but open-minded, I began to study turkey tail mushroom as a supplement. After the ceaseless emotional highs and lows my family and I had gone through in the previous months, I was unwilling to subscribe to any treatment that I had not personally researched and prayed about. So, I dug a bit further and found this particular ingredient had many beneficial attributes documented in the naturopathic medical research realms. For example, it has been shown to reduce inflammation, boost the immune system, support a healthy gut, assist in balancing blood sugar, help preserve cognitive performance as people age, facilitate healthy urinary tract maintenance, and aid in fighting cancer.[4]

Fighting cancer…? Really? Something as common and accessible as a mushroom has the power to do that?

I averted my eyes from the screen for a moment and glanced down at my legs. They were throbbing from a recent therapy romp. Was it even *remotely* possible that something as innocuous as a fungus on the forest floor could have prevented everything I was going through?

As I continued my reading, I came across reports stating that the polysaccharide krestin and polysaccharide peptide in these mushrooms support—and can increase the efficacy of—cancer treatments and radiation.[5] The information available was plentiful once a person started digging. One study I stumbled onto by way of the National Library of Medicine even stated that "medicinal mushrooms have the potential to prevent lymph node metastasis, prolong overall survival, decrease chemotherapy-induced side effects (e.g., diarrhea, vomiting), affect the immune system, and help maintain immune function and quality of life in patients with certain cancers."[6]

Prevent metastasis? Decrease the horror-show side-effects of chemo? Help the immunity system? All this from a mushroom?!

It was hard to believe that this one plant wasn't already a staple in every cancer patient's daily regimen if it did all those things. The whole wide world could take it from me: Cancer makes you *very* sick and weak. I would have taken *anything* that would have helped with those issues, even a little!

Of course, I didn't want to be naïve and just believe the first thing I read online, either. There was the question of whether these articles had perhaps been exaggerated by the authors who had a personal agenda… though I couldn't imagine what that would be. These studies were *not* being reported on a supplement site with a natural bias for selling their own products. They were just scientists documenting the features of a plant through peer review. Maybe the mushrooms *were* amazing, but just not quite amazing enough to make the difference in cancer treatment. After all, it's *cancer* we're talking about. The biggie… The impenetrable killer.

But then again, here was this man and his mother in the video I had watched, standing in front of the audience they were addressing at the filmed convention they were speaking at, celebrating her continued life, years after the prognosis had *spoken death over her*.

That was encouraging to see…

My search went on. In the days ahead, having been rendered physically unable to engage in much activity, I found that the time on my hands became well-spent in this exploration of alternative cancer treatments. After pondering turkey tail mushroom for a few days, I continued to read numerous reports of people claiming to have cured cancer using a variety of products ranging from herbal supplements to veterinary and even equine medication products (in particular, de-wormers and anti-parasite medications). While some of the stories told by those claiming their healing came through products made for animals were compelling, I shied away from such remedies because: a) they were not made for human consumption (and I was in over my head starting a regimen like that without a doctor to help me do so safely); and b) I didn't have the first idea how to determine dosage, since the dosages on those labels assume the remedy is being administered to an animal of a far different size and weight.

Yet, while my search trekked onward, I was surprised during this period to find that many traditional medical doctors who had come forward with information about natural means of treating cancer had seen their videos removed, websites taken down, or otherwise been shadow-banned.

Huh…what's that about?

This piqued my curiosity and partially confirmed I was onto something… If these doctors were all just unorthodox crackpots and phonies, then why would "the powers that be" care if their teachings were online? Why not just let them keep rambling about natural stuff until they get bored of blowing smoke or until they hung themselves with their own rope of lies? They weren't hurting anyone by telling cancer patients to eat mushrooms… Could it be that someone (or a lot of someones they call "Big Pharma") high up in the Western system was pulling censorship levers online? And if so, why? Because something in these naturalistic presentations would actually work to help people overcome their cancer and therefore become a threat to the "business side" of Western pharmaceuticals?

I don't know. I suppose I'll never know. But, whatever the reason: The more these innocuous, harmless, natural cancer treatment presentations online disappeared, the more I dug in that direction. A man would post his findings about how an ingredient half of Americans put on their salad might help cure disease, and something about it would be too threatening to allow it to *remain* posted…and that was just far too suspicious to me to ignore.

Is that where You want me, God? I see You flagging me. Is that where You are?

As I listened to what these doctors were saying, I would make notes of the products, ingredients, or supplements that they were discussing, and then I would go to reputable online medical journals and type the name of the element into their search engine. Often, even the medical journals, themselves, would acknowledge that the element was believed to help in some way toward healing cancer or boosting the efficacy of cancer-fighting medical interventions.

Lord, these are doctors. WESTERN doctors—are they not? These are the peers of the folks who work in facilities similar to those I've sought help from. If they are openly acknowledging these plants to be of assistance in battling cancer, why don't more doctors know about them? Why aren't they trained in these details?

I thought about Dr. Ibrahim. I knew for certain and beyond the shadow of any doubt that if her medical training had prepared her with this knowledge, she would have told me. She cared about me. I *knew* she did.

Father, there are doctors that would make this a part of their practice if these plants had been a part of their education and training. It's like this information is hidden. Why? I mean, we can find it if we look hard enough, and when we do *find it, it's legitimate medical research, but it's buried under endless oceans of materials endorsing chemotherapy. Why?*

During that time, my headspace began to shift. My perspective regarding continued medical treatment began to irreversibly change. I knew—and doctors had confirmed—that unless God intervened, the path I was on was one of certain death. Further, the end would be preceded by a terrible journey of continued pain and suffering for myself *and* my loved ones before it was over. I was never one to go down without a fight, but I also understood that this battle would never be won within my own strength. Ultimately, this entire situation was outside of my own control.

Take your chemo pills, Fearful Lynette repeated throughout the day.

Should I, though?

But *God* was still in control. The same God who made my body. The One who knew the outcome of this battle before He ever custom-knitted me in my mother's womb (Psalm 139:13). The One who has already numbered my days and my nights (Psalm 37:18). The One who, even as my son was shaving my beautiful dreadlocks from my exhausted, suffering head, had taken the time to number each of the hairs on it (Luke 12:7). The One who has gone before me and stands guard behind me (Psalm 139:5), whose hand was laid upon me during my formation and who has made me fearfully and wonderfully, regardless of this ominous illness (Psalm 139:14).

Meditating on these thoughts about the Divine, I pulled out my phone and recorded a short video for my own personal library. Regardless of what I would choose to do with the medication situation, I wanted a visual reminder that, for a follower of Christ, healing starts with faith, and faith is "the substance of things hoped for, the evidence of things not seen" (Hebrews 11:1). If I hoped for an outcome that defied what my very own eyes were telling me about my disease-riddled body, it would start by speaking *life* from my own lips, even if those words could be interpreted as denial by the secular world. The Bible is clear that "even God, who quickeneth the dead…calleth those things which be not as though they were" (Romans 4:17); in other words, the same God with the power to raise the dead calls forth and materializes *His own* realities. In line with that, I recorded myself speaking affirmations: I was already healed because God had said it would be; I was already healthy, I just needed to catch up to the Lord.

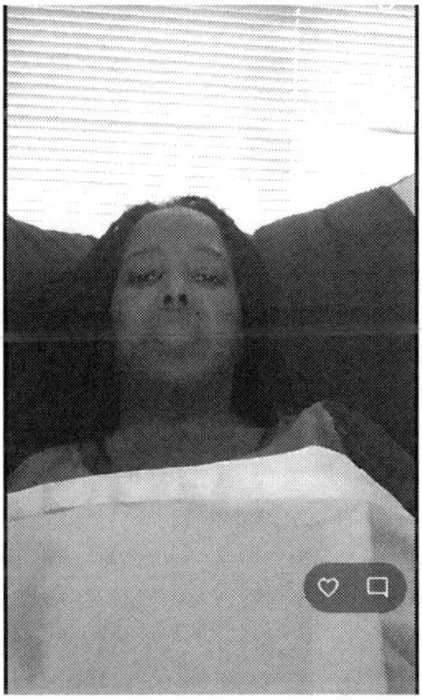

Me, speaking life into my body in a personal affirmation video just before my radical healing. Though this was never meant to be a public video, the next one would place my testimony into the hands of millions.

Despite this, Fearful Lynette kept grasping for my attention.

Take your pills…

Hush. I'm thinking.

Without the miraculous intervention of my Creator, I knew how the journey would end. Ultimately, my life was in the hands of the one and only One: the same God who had designed my body in the first place. Would that potential intervention I was praying for come through chemotherapy, as I had thought for so many weeks in the beginning? Or maybe, just maybe, was there a chance it would come through something natural, as I had begun to feel convicted about in the last few weeks?

Take your pills…

Maybe I shouldn't, Faithful Lynette resisted.

You heard your doctors! Your chemo pills are the only thing keeping you alive, and you're starting to doubt whether you should take them at all? If you think like that, you'll die!

How do you know what "thinking" will do to me? You won't let me think at all. Seriously, hush.

However, I had my family to think about with every move I made, and I was aware that I live in a culture wherein a person with my diagnosis receives a certain type of protocol, and "it would be *crazy*" to challenge those well-established rules. That's simply what it boiled down to. The "sane" person was expected to follow a designed treatment. Some doctors might even state that the treatment they prescribe is "mandatory" for anyone who wants a fighting chance at survival. I was all too aware that my family, doctors, and loved ones would insist that I dedicate the time I had left to rigidly following all outlined strategies of chemotherapy, or any other cancer-fighting medical interventions that I had access to through my regular doctors. And, most of all, I knew that these treatments, designed to extend or even save life, held a good chance of *stealing the quality of the life they may or may not extend in the first place.*

Take your pills.

…

Hey, aren't you listening? Take your chemo pills.

…

What, you're ignoring me now? Take your pills!

"Nothing man-made or man-prescribed is guaranteed to save me at this point, Lord," I prayed. "Nothing. The chemo is guaranteed to make me miserably sick and take away chances I had to enjoy my family in these latter days, but that's about all it guarantees. This journey might be something different for someone else, but in *my* case, I'm the 'incurable stage four.' God, the *best-case scenario* on these harsh, intense Western cancer medicines is that I prolong my inevitable death for a few months, a year or two if I get handed a miracle, but getting my life back on these is out of the question."

With my inner fear causing a racket in the background, I took a deep breath and considered John, my siblings, and my children. My eyes fell on the windowsill. The trees outside were lush and green. The breeze tickled them and they tittered in response, shuffling their leaves about. I knew if I was standing right next to them, I would be able to hear the rustling noise of their bubbly laughter—laughter that was so untouched, so unconcerned, with disease. Yet they had but one Caretaker.

How was it that they were so healthy? Why were all the plants throughout all the world so, *so* healthy? Of course, there had been plagues or mankind's pollution that had introduced an *unnatural* sort of cancer or disease to some of the planet's vegetation (which now reminds me of certain Western medicines), but leaving nature to simply do what nature does ended in…everything thriving in beauty always.

"Lord, is it even possible that *Your* regimen actually *would* give me my life back?"

In my gut—no—*in my spirit,* I knew that, unless I did something drastic, my family was going to bury me, and soon. However, I *also* knew that any decision I made to move into a more natural treatment plan would be met with fear and concern that I was compromising my chances of survival.

You ARE compromising your chances of survival. Take your pills! Listen to the voice of reason!

You know what, Faithful Lynette said with so much authority it almost shocked even me. *You're not the voice of reason. You're the voice of fear. And you don't help me; you hinder me. You always have. Now I'm going to speak to my God for a moment and you're not going to interrupt me again.*

My pulse increased just a little. The atmosphere shifted again, just like it did when Cislyn prayed for me that day God spoke through her to tell me He "was *going to*" heal me. A confidence swelled within me at the rebuke of my inner fear and, with its quick departure, I felt a surge of faith and excitement take its place. With a clear, clean line of communication between myself and God—now lacking the static that always buzzed about when fear was allowed to speak—I looked at the oral chemotherapy and wondered if aborting it from my daily regimen might be part of how that healing touch would come.

Such a small thing, isn't it, God? One tiny little oval tablet, one half inch in length, one quarter inch in width, and living in a push-blister pack with living quarters less significant in size than my pinkie nail…and yet, it has the power to do all the damage it's done to me. And, if I continue on it, it may even be the dagger that kills me. But, for all that, it doesn't have the power to save me, does it?

I thought back to the night I received Dr. Bakir's phone call. I remembered how it felt the first time I received the news that the six-letter assassin was creeping through *my* veins, *my* halls, poisoning me while I slept, and doing so silently, so the damage wouldn't be found until I was already too far gone to be helped. I recalled my first personal consideration of Cancer's "mighty challenger," Chemo, knowing through the grapevine and the rumor mill—though not yet through experience—that it was its own monster to be feared. Together, they hailed down certain doom. While Cancer menacingly teases the seething, serpentine beast awake until it stirs and rises to feast fully upon the unwary, Chemo attempts to smoke Cancer and his pet out with toxic gas—a gas that has the potential to kill both Cancer and the beast...but leave *no* survivor in its wake.

Then, as if all at once in a moment of complete and total clarity, the smell of death was upon them both.

Chemo was no champion to me anymore.

He was Cancer's *partner.*

How have I not seen this before?

I imagined myself in my mind's eye, putting the smooth chemotherapy pill past my lower lip and onto my tongue, closing my lips around it, and rinsing it past the gullet with water...and, for the first time, I was revolted by the very idea. To intentionally, *purposefully* take that poison into my body, my *temple,* suddenly felt wrong to me. I winced, blinked, and swallowed a lump in my throat. I didn't look in the mirror in that moment, but if I had, I'm sure I would have seen a very disgusted expression on my features.

Father God, it may not be the same decision everyone else would make, but it's mine. This isn't right. Chemotherapy isn't right!

In that moment, I made a decision: one sealed with fervent prayer. For me, it was time to relinquish the rigid regimen of medical treatments and interventions—all that fuss that simply didn't amount to much besides beating up my weary body further—and instead embark upon a journey of faith. It was a radical, countercultural decision, made staring into the eyes of an indiscriminate harbinger of death in a world that puts its trust in conventional medicine.

But I was convinced that it was precisely what the Maker of my body was telling me to do next:

I would trade trust in the standard medical process for faith in the Creator of all.

I would forsake the perception of safety and rates of survival, instead embracing the odds of alternative forms of treatment.

In a world where people walk by sight, I would walk by faith (2 Corinthians 5:7).

I would listen to the Ultimate Physician, the One who knows my body better than any doctor.

In a world where society turns to doctors to offer them hope of healing, I would turn to the Ultimate Healer (Psalm 41:3).

This would be my new countercultural journey of faith. *This* is where I would place my hope.

This was my new cancer treatment.

As a new resolution and attitude toward my continued pursuit of healing solidified in my heart, I said a prayer regarding the natural, plant-sourced treatments I was beginning to find information about.

"God, these are all things that You created. You said that the plants of the earth were given to man for our benefit; the herbs bearing seeds, and the fruits of the trees [Genesis 1:29]. You also told us to come boldly into the throne room, seeking help in our time of need [Hebrews 4:16]. And, You *also* said, while we are in this fleshly body, we are absent from You, but, to be absent from the body is to be present with the Lord [2 Corinthians 5:6–8]."

Fearful Lynette had stopped blabbing several minutes prior, yet I was so honed in on following God with faith that I hadn't noticed my inner fear had ceased, leaving in its vacancy a peace that truly did surpass all understanding, guarding my heart and mind in the Blood of Jesus (Philippians 4:7). I continued my prayerful commitment.

"Being in this body is temporary in the first place, but without Your mercy, my time in this body is perhaps more limited than it should be. So, I'm placing my trust in You. Show me how to find healing. Show me, Lord! I'm listening. Lead me to what I should and should not put in this vessel You've given me and I will be bold, stop all of these other poisons, and treat my bodily tissues with the plants *You* made for medicine."

Before I lost myself in emotion, I collected myself for one more plea—a plea that would elevate my prayer, remove the human from the equation, and put God back in His rightful place of control.

"God, my life has always been, and is now, in Your hands. What happens next is up to You. Either heal me, or—" my breath shuddered and caught in my throat. I willed myself to finish my petition: "Either heal me, or take me home."

This prayer became my New Year's resolution for the year 2022, which was only a day or two away. I decided that on New Year's Day—a date on the calendar I could always remember for comparison and tracking progress—I would quietly put away all pharmaceutical medications and begin a natural path toward healing.

I decided not to confide in my loved ones regarding this choice…at least not immediately: I knew that this radical decision of mine would only incite fear and concern for my wellbeing, especially from John, who had already been through so much. I *never* kept secrets from John, my constant, my pillar, my best friend. But I decided to insulate him from something I knew was guaranteed to raise alarm. I had been so close to death for so long that my passing wouldn't have surprised anyone, *but*, if this radical, natural protocol *worked*—I mean, if I could actually pull this off—then the thing nobody expected, *my survival*, could be celebrated later. It may not have been a perfect decision but, at the time, it was my best effort to protect him from even more suffering.

I continued to research and ask God to lead me to the products, supplements, or ingredients that He would have me use. It was the biggest step of faith I have ever taken in the whole of my earthly life, but it felt completely *right*. For the first time in so long on this cancer journey, I felt excitement about where my body would be in the coming weeks: as if Warrior-Lynette had just taken over—and not just in physical therapy, but in every aspect. No matter what was coming, how hard or painful it would be, or whether there was another barefoot-on-a-sea-of-glass challenge on the horizon, I was determined to put my life in God's hands and let *His* medicines carry me from then on.

However, just because I had decided to pivot to natural healing does not mean that I ran to the Internet and ordered every ingredient linked to someone's naturopathic cancer-free story. In fact, at that point in time, my frame had been reduced to skin and bones, and the nausea was so bad that I was leery of pumping my system full of too many new components my body would then be forced to process. The decision to go natural had been made, but precisely which new remedies to take on remained undecided.

December 2021, posing with my photographer friend Aubre just days before switching to the natural protocol for good; when this photo was taken, neither of us imagined he would one day photograph me for the cover of this book that tells the miraculous story of my radical restoration!

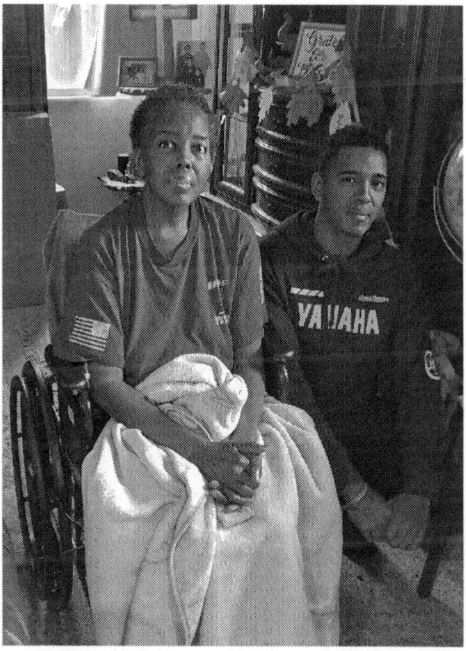

December 2021, visiting with my son Adam while bound to a wheelchair merely days before God's medicine would begin to reverse the disease in my veins

Chapter Seventeen

RIGHTEOUS ANGER FINDS THE TRIFECTA

As impressed as I had been about the information I found regarding turkey tail mushrooms, I actually did not end up going in that direction. The introduction to their healing potential had been vital to my journey, as the knowledge of them redirected me *away* from standard medicine, but as I continued to pray about them, something in my spirit told me to keep looking. I was closer to seeing God and His waving flags after hearing about turkey tail, but that is where my relationship with them ended.

Continuing the search, I determined that when God had brought me to the right regimen for me, He would make that clear. The diligent mission continued for a matter of days, when I stumbled onto a quote that resonated in my gut in a way that I couldn't shake. It was allegedly spoken by the Prophet Muhammad: "The black seed can heal every disease, except death."[7]

Every disease but death, huh? Compelling…

I only needed a cure for cancer. Not that this was any small request. But as I kept digging, I found reports conducted by medical journals stating that this "black seed" supplement *had* been found effective against cancer.

I'm not sure what specifically stuck with me about the "everything but death" quote, but it lingered in my mind. I prayed about it while continuing to look into the healing attributes of black seed, sometimes also called "black cumin" or "black cumin seed." The materials I read on it discussed its ability to serve in *many* medicinal capacities. Not only was it hailed as a cancer-fighter, it had also been linked to improving cardiovascular health and mediating certain cardiovascular difficulties, helping the body prevent and fight diabetes, improving kidney health, and intervening in such lung ailments as asthma.

To share only one example of what I found on the apparent miracle-seed, a study from the *African Journal of Traditional, Complementary, and Alternative Medicines* reported that black cumin "is effective against cancer in [the] blood system, lung, kidney, liver, prostate, breast, cervix, [and] skin with much safety."[8] Unlike many of the other remedies I had read about but decided to forego, this one sounded like a part of the new regimen that God was leading me to.

As I mulled prayerfully over the notion of black seed for a few days, feeling a stronger pull toward it every minute that passed, I stumbled onto another plant-based ingredient that many people were claiming had helped them overcome cancer: the soursop leaf. This particular leaf caught my attention when I happened upon a testimony shared by a young married couple: The wife had, like me, been diagnosed with cancer and was losing the battle quickly. Her time on earth was limited—as mine had been announced to be. She and her husband decided to visit some islands as a last getaway to enjoy her remaining days together, but while they were on this tropical vacation, a native islander told the couple about soursop, which grows wild in that particular part of the world. Feeling they had nothing to lose, they decided to try it and, over time, her health made a turnaround and her cancer was *cured.*

There was something familiar, almost comforting, about the idea of trying something from around my own homeland. Out of curiosity, I phoned my brother, Peter, to ask him if he had heard about this miracle supplement.

The phone rang a few times, and then I heard his memorable, warm voice answer. When I greeted him, the thick Caribbean accent rang out, "Hello, sister! How are you doing today?"

Peter is the type of person who, when he asks how you are doing, he waits for a *real* answer to the question, unwilling to settle for the quick "I'm fine" many others are satisfied with. My precious brother and I speak often, and he shows genuine concern and love for me and the others in our family. He sends me positive affirmations and Scriptures, and always shows how much he cares, despite his somewhat stoic and serious demeanor. When I revealed the reason for my call, he informed me that he had indeed heard of the soursop leaf.

"But here we call it bush tea," he said, adding, "I take it myself because it helps me sleep."

Maybe it was the warmth of Peter's voice, or the indirect connection to home I seemed to feel through the concept of the soursop leaf. Either way, I have no doubt it was God's direction that brought me to this peculiar, and evidently wonderful, leaf. As I sat there in my room, hooked up to the IV bag filled with nutrients, I once again looked around, letting my eyes fall back to that window as the afternoon sun gleamed through the glass. My body was uncomfortable, my PICC line required me to stay in the most obnoxiously rigid position, my legs were in a state of being sore almost around the clock from continued physical therapy, and, other than having my sweet brother on the other end of the line, I was as alone as I had ever been. But that leaf…somehow the idea of bringing something from my happiest home made me feel less lonely, less homesick, less… vulnerable, perhaps.

Peter encouraged me to try the soursop tea, which didn't surprise me because he is always so supportive. I spent the following days continuing to read about this wondrous herb, finding reports confirming it to be effective against not only a *variety* of cancers, but also in combatting convulsions, arthritis, parasites, and even malaria. Additionally, it is documented to be helpful in controlling diabetes, gastric conditions, and ulcers, and, as my brother had noted, it was effective for those struggling with insomnia.[9] Other reports discussed its naturally high content of vitamin C, crediting this property for being one of the many reasons that soursop *also* strengthens the immune system![10] According to articles published by the National Institute of Health (NIH), "soursop leaves endophytic fungi extracts showed cytotoxicity against cervical cancer cells,"[11] and the soursop plant "produces edible fruit all year round and is widely used as a traditional medicine for skin disease, respiratory disease, fever, bacterial infections, diabetes, hypertension, and *cancer*."[12]

That is only a *few* of the dozens and dozens of articles regarding the power of the soursop leaf I found along my journey. After prayerful consideration, I decided that soursop tea would officially be one of the items I would add to the new regimen that I—with God's help—was building.

Then came the apricot kernels…those seeds occasionally blasted online for being "toxic." After consuming them, the cyanogenic glycosides (naturally occurring plant compounds derived from amino acids) convert to cyanide within the human body.

Was it really smart for a person in my immunocompromised position to be taking something like *that*?

For a minute, I hesitated (and my greatest enemy, Cancer, would have loved it if I would have redirected my browser right then and there). However, with what I had gone through in taking chemotherapy, I had a newfound understanding for what "toxic" really felt like—and, once again, I had nothing to lose—so I dug a little deeper than the scary words. That's when I noticed that the same sources warning folks about the cyanide also admit that it's only when you consume over a certain amount that this becomes a concern.

How much is too much? I wondered.

I found the answer fairly early on: It depends on your personal body weight; what is safe for an adult to consume is not safe for a child to consume and so on. So, assuming I could calculate a safe dose for my size and remain restricted to that, then maybe it wouldn't be…

Wait a second. Isn't that how *all* medicines work? Literally all of them, including over-the-counter drugs? Medicine labels have safe dosage instructions printed on them and it's up to the consumer to swallow responsibly. If there are any exceptions to that, then it's news to me. If a consumer buys himself a bottle of acetaminophen pain relievers, ignores all the safety warnings, and consumes a mouthful at once, something as innocuous as Tylenol is "toxic," too. In fact, acetaminophen overdose results in "56,000 emergency department visits, 2,600 hospitalizations, and 500 deaths each year" in the United States *alone*, half of which occurred by accident.[13] But the medical field doesn't put articles up warning people to steer clear of "toxic Tylenol." They warn to stick to the dosage, but how and why was that different with apricot kernels? Why did there appear to be such discouragement around taking them if they actually *could* help cure something as horrific as cancer?

Was it because someone in the pharmaceutical industry found the kernels to be a threat to their business?

I would never dedicate enough time in my life to investigating every Big Pharma conspiracy that floated around on the Internet, so it's likely I'd never have the answer to that question. Be that as it may, however, I was starting to see yet another tier to how Big Pharma was controlling the mainstream narrative: It wasn't just about *hiding* information on natural-healing ingredients, it was about openly discussing them so they could look transparent in the public eye while dressing the supplements in language that made them appear to hold a particular, *unique* threat to human safety…when, in reality, they generally shared the same "overdose" threat common to *all* medications.

Sneaky…

In any case, this particular cancer-fighter may not need to frighten me away. At the very least, it couldn't have been as harsh on my body as the *other* cancer-fighter, chemotherapy…not by a mile.

Early on, I watched a testimonial, wherein a man talked about the numerous health benefits and cancer-fighting agents in these seeds. He went on and on, well past the point I thought he would wrap it up, yet the glowing recommendation continued. As I continued to learn, a wealth of good information was unearthed from respected sources, and the benefits amazed me. The National Institute of Health, for instance, reported myriad of attributes for the apricot kernel, including as an aid against breast cancer, cardiovascular issues, asthma, insomnia, gastric problems, and many other health difficulties.[14] Not to mention, these hefty seeds are "used in the preparation of various medicines," offer anti-carcinogenic potential compounds, help to reduce gastric mucosal inflammation, and provide a variety of effective fibers which even help lower cholesterol![15]

It looked as though I had another piece of the protocol-puzzle put together.

In the thick of it all, I decided to run some of these ideas past Dr. Bakir to see if he had ever heard whether these ingredients may have had positive results for others in my situation. And who knows… Maybe he would have another suggestion of an ingredient or healing method to add to my current list.

I called and left a message, and within a day or two he returned my call with a straightforward and fairly dire warning: 1) I was not to follow *any* natural protocols or healing methods because they simply do not work; 2) some supplements can make the whole cancer treatment situation worse as they can negatively interact with chemotherapy medications; 3) he had not heard of soursop tea or black seed, but apricot kernels are "toxic" and

I was putting myself at risk to take them, or anything else that wasn't prescribed by either my oncologist or himself.

The respect that I have for Dr. Bakir is legitimate and sincere. It's not the kind of flippant, lip-service "respect" that is commonly lurking beneath sayings like, "With all due respect, [fill-in-the-blank frustration, rebuttal, or defense]." I honestly appreciate him as a person, a professional, and a caregiver to people. If *he* says not to take something, I do believe it's because he genuinely doesn't want to see one of his patients get hurt, and I'm certain doctors see people self-sabotaging all the time by putting weird or stupid things in their body because a lay-article or meme online suggested it. I know his resistance to these ingredients was out of concern for my welfare—and if, as he said, he wasn't familiar with them outside of hearing words like "toxic," he would be operating outside of his license and practice experience to a) withhold warnings about toxicity and b) tell me to proceed. So, I *do* understand and value his motive for discouraging me and the time he took to deliver that discouragement. No harm, no foul.

But we did not agree. I believed God led me thus far, and I was proceeding with or without Dr. Bakir's sanctioning.

Ravenously, I dug through the Internet, drinking in site after site, paying less attention to unqualified or amateur sources, and keeping my focus on the peer-reviewed, scientific journal reports. Time and again, the wonderful things I had been hearing about these ingredients I had chosen were bolstered by other studies in recent years. I ordered books by experts and, while barely out of the mail packaging, devoured them rapidly. I wanted to know everything there was to know about how I might naturally combat my diagnosis, my prognosis...the death that the Western world had spoken over me. Yet a distracting conundrum was now demanding more of my attention: One *can* find information by true-blue scientists and medical specialists in the field of cancer supporting natural healing methods. It certainly was out there. But for every one scholarly journal, study, or report I found that validated plant-based protocols, probably *hundreds* of other articles endorsing Western chemotherapy fought for dominance across my screen...many of which were written in such a way as to instill fear into the minds of the readers by telling them all the horrible things that will happen to them if they went off their meds before they were told by their doctor to do so.

The more I researched, the more frustrated I became at how seemingly *intentional* the burial of good information was on the subject of natural healing. It appeared, on my end, *many* deaths were possibly unnecessary!; that trusting, fearful patients were following a treatment protocol assigned to them while they were never made aware of the fact (and yes, it was now becoming a *fact*) that there may be other healthier options out there! Options that may very well provide a longer and more comfortable life than traditional, Western treatments auto-fed to these sweet, dying people on the daily by folks who mean well but don't have time to stop and see the *astounding, multiple layers of evidence even within their own medical community!*

Every time I noticed an outspoken doctor who advocated for natural treatments being silenced; every time I went to re-watch a testimonial video just to find it removed; every time I realized another spokesperson for natural remedies had been shadow-banned, my determination to follow my newfound path of healing became more solidified in my soul. It was a path paved in prayer, faith, and trust in my Lord, but it was also becoming fueled by the righteous anger that bubbled up at the thought that someone, somewhere high up on the ladder of importance in Big Pharma, was intentionally hiding *God's* medicine.

Even Jesus, Himself, got angry when He saw the Father's house turned into a "den of thieves" (Matthew 21:12–16). Think about that a moment. Don't rush the scene. It's far more relevant than one might initially assume.

There they were, in the first century, with Jewish pilgrims coming in from all over the ancient world, bringing the most spotless lamb from their herd to sacrifice in the Temple in observation of the Passover feast. After a long and heavy history of war, domination, and slavery between the Jewish people and the surrounding nations, an enormous number of Jews were impoverished in ways we modern folks can't even imagine. Still, they poured their money, time, and shepherding talent into raising and grooming their sacrificial lambs, and then transporting them all the way from their homes to Jerusalem for the annual gathering. Then, *if* the scholars who have pieced this story together are correct: 1) the Jews would line up at the Temple to have their sheep approved for sacrifice; 2) the dubious religious leaders inspecting the sheep for perfection would find any tiny micro-offense on their skin, wool, legs, ears, etc. (and if there wasn't a blemish to be found, some scholars believe they would make something up), intentionally rendering the animals unfit for sacrifice; 3) the head of those Jewish households (i.e., the victim of the scam) had no choice at that time but to agree to give an exorbitant amount of money—*and* the "blemished" lambs they brought with them—for one of the pre-approved sheep in the pen near the religious leaders; 4) after the Jews who had just been scammed had walked away, the religious leaders would usher the "blemished" lamb to the back of the line in the pen, eventually to be presented as one of the pre-approved, spotless lambs to Jews several spaces down in the line.

Meanwhile, because the secular money of the Romans had been stamped with pagan gods and rulers, religious leaders would not accept any coin that wasn't their own Jewish currency because a pagan coin would blaspheme or desecrate the Temple grounds. Any Jew arriving in Jerusalem had to first visit the money-changing booths to get their own pagan currency changed over to the holy and acceptable Temple currency for an unusually hefty exchange fee. The religious leaders knew these Jews were away from home and very vulnerable, so they hiked up the fees to take the Jewish travelers for all they were worth.

Between the blemished-sheep/pre-approved sheep scam and the cruel fees of the money-changers, God's Temple—a place of *blessing* that had been intended to bring God's people closer to Him—had become a place of exploitation, shrewd business, and con-artistry. Instead of the pilgrims concentrating upon spiritual things, many of them (especially the poor) were beginning to dread the annual trip across harsh roads and under the blistering sun for miles and miles with both animal and human to feed and look after in the caravan…just to arrive and get swindled by the "holy men" who were supposed to be the supreme Jewish example.

I can see why Jesus, upon His arrival to the Temple to observe this trickery in person, got fueled by righteous anger, overturned the tables, and chased the con artists away. But it's the "why" in this equation that is most relevant for our reflection here: 1) He couldn't stand that the poorest of His brethren were being taken advantage of; 2) God's house is *the last place* these kinds of dubious dealings should occur; 3) these religious leaders made God's house appear to be the opposite of what it really was (from a place of blessing to a place of sabotage and distrust).

If Western medicine is attempting to conceal the true benefits of God's plants and, instead, offer up lab-created treatments that are far more harmful—*all the while charging an exorbitant amount to the patient who is already inundated with bills*—is this not a modernized idea of the same wicked spirit that Jesus rebuked in this powerful New Testament scene? Affordable, healthy disease-fighters like mushrooms, tea leaves, or seeds are ushered to the back of the "pen," while the tricksters bring out "spotless" Western prescriptions (some of which truly are poisonous) for hefty fees. All the while, I can only imagine: 1) God is angry that the poorest of His children are being taken advantage of: 2) a place of healing the sick is the *last place* these kinds of dubious dealings should occur; 3) these religious leaders made God's own medicines appear to be the opposite of what they really are (from a low-cost blessing to a dangerous "alternative medicine" that should be avoided at all costs, hidden, concealed, rejected by the medical community, and all endorsements behind these ingredients should be shadow-banned, taken down…)

Don't you readers see how comparative these scenarios are? What many of the "powers that be" behind Big Pharma appear to be doing is a great injustice. In my view, they are setting themselves up to be the keeper of the keys to healing, the *only* avenue through which a person can get help for sickness and pain, and they're passing out the medicine that keeps these people sick enough to always *remain* vulnerably dependent. What a "sick" cycle, indeed (angry, ironic pun intended)…

Though it's true I had not yet put all this together to this degree back when the righteous anger first hit me during these early days of my natural healing epiphanies, I felt something was questionable about all of it. Research, prayer, knowledge, and spiritual maturity would bring me to a place where I could more properly identify and label my anger against the system as I have outlined herein. The comparisons are simply too glaring to ignore. And if Jesus became angered, then I still believe to this day that I am justified in feeling anger boiling beneath my skin over those who label God's medicine "dangerous" while they deal in poisons! And that is especially true when I see a person suffering in unfathomable pain as a side effect of chemotherapy, which, to me, will now always be a harsh *pretender*: A wolf-in-sheep's-clothing counterfeit "medicine" that may affirmatively kill cancer cells, while it also kills the body's good cells right along with them, and there *might simply be another, healthier way*!

If nothing else, I pray God helps me channel these passionate feelings of mine about natural treatments into reaching others who are just as blockaded from knowing the truth as I once was. If nothing else ever came from my terrible experience on chemotherapy, I would be happy knowing that I suffered so someone else may not have to.

Now, the only thing that sat between my confidence in natural healing and my celebration of its efficacy was time. It was one thing to truly hold faith in every crevice of my heart, soul, and mind that God had led me to the medicines that could be trusted to heal me. But it was a whole other thing being able to irrefutably prove that to others—an event I now believed would happen when my wrecked, near-dead body had been given time to repair itself from the damage the cancer and chemotherapy had done in their deadly tag-team match against my tissues. First and foremost, I needed to get on, and stay on, the new regimen.

I prepared the short list and asked my husband to take me to the natural food and herbal supplements store in our town. Like I said before, I did not mention my decision to discontinue my medical treatments to him at this time; I only told him that I would like to look into natural healing. Ever supportive and loving, John readily agreed to take me. My new medications list, prayerfully obtained, included only three simple items—black seed oil, soursop tea leaves, and apricot kernels—no additional additives or fuss.

Arriving at our local natural grocery and herbal supply market, my precious husband dutifully pushed my wheelchair inside where the powerful blend of herbal scents characteristic of such a store greeted us upon arrival. On a mission, we only briefly took in the ambient setting, but it was memorable: family-owned and "hole in the wall" small, but homey and comfortable, as if it had been the rooted "herbal medicine man" establishment in this community for decades.

Moving toward the consultation desk near the checkout aisles, we pivoted around the kiosks at the front of the store, which offered a variety of potential last-minute additions to a person's purchase. At the front of the lane, which was lined on either side by a variety of vitamins and natural supplements, stood a small help-desk where a person could ask an employee for guidance regarding herbal products and their benefits. The owner stood there, a kind and patient man who, alongside his wife, had owned and operated the store for a number of years. He smiled when I explained the reason for my visit to him, and then he thumped an enormous book down upon the desktop in front of me, boasting that it was like an herbalist's Bible. Inside its pages, he assured me, was the answer to all my questions.

As I continued to fill him in on the details of my personal situation, the man consulted his tome, bringing confirmation to—and thus, confidence behind—the research I had already done at home. It wasn't necessarily a fast process, but the man endured it kindly. His gentle nature brought me comfort, and his willingness to go through such a long list of questions with me reassured me on many levels that I was on the right track. Ultimately, I left the store having purchased apricot kernels and black seed oil, but the soursop leaves had to wait until I could get them in their whole, pure, untouched form (as this store only had them dried and ground in teabags with other ingredients).

Shortly thereafter, with trifecta in hand, the clock struck twelve o'clock in the morning on January 1, 2022. In an instant, my life entered a new chapter—a heightened journey of faith. By researching and developing resolve, I had already embarked upon this voyage, but now, the time had come to place action behind the mind-frame I had entered and set up my canvas of proof. One day, hopefully, the rest of the world would be able to gaze upon that natural health canvas and be encouraged that God *is* in control, He *did* account for sickness when He made all of Creation, and that He *will* reward faithful adherence to His voice, even when those acts of obedience are carried out in direct opposition to the mainstream societal and cultural narratives regarding truth and reality.

As we bid 2021 farewell and welcomed 2022, I, likewise, said goodbye forever to the old treatment regimen and prepared for the full measure of God's healing to fall upon my body, my heart, and my life. The next year would bring both blessings and challenges, but I was up for both and either. So assured was I in the new direction I had taken in my medical journey that challenges would, I now knew, only end in making me stronger. It was a win-win, and I was going into it with eager anticipation.

January 2022,
just beginning the natural protocol

The changes that occurred throughout my body upon switching to a plant-based protocol may not have been immediate, but within only weeks and months, they were noticeable…beginning with my legs.

Physical therapy continued for a while to be an excruciating process. Between the loss of muscular strength I once had and the added neuropathy that I gained through my near-death experience, I worked hard and endured much stinging, throbbing, and lengthy muscle soreness for each step my body had to re-learn, like a toddler, to take under my body weight. As my upright, standing balance slowly returned to me, I thanked God for the progress, but I kept fighting for more gains in this area so that I might someday be able to walk again without assistance from walkers, therapists, and other assists. Thank goodness God allowed me to get in touch with Warrior-Lynette just when I did, because that day gave me the vigor to strive for the kind of improvement that can only come through facing discomfort head-on.

Day after day, my pain diminished incrementally, and my strength increased. The original, five-step goal of physical therapy quickly grew into the pursuit of ten steps, and then twenty. By the end of six weeks, I was able to take twenty steps completely unassisted, and the piercing, pins-and-needles sensation in my feet was slowly, but steadily, fading. This was a miracle in itself, as I had been told by various medical personnel that the pain was caused by nerve damage they did *not* expect to heal. Eventually, I was able to switch from being wheelchair-bound to getting around with a walker.

But that was probably just because physical therapy works when patients take it seriously…right? It didn't have anything to do with going natural. No, probably not. It did feel amazing, though, dipping my toes in the pool of strength again.

Of course, it wasn't just my ability to get around that improved.

There was the unexpected, but intensely relieving, return to digestive regularity. When the mass had grown up and throughout the center of my body, the obstacle that it presented (along with the surrounding inflammation) served to create a blockage that my body struggled to work around when it was time for waste-evacuation. In the earlier days of my natural treatment plan, I wasn't certain exactly *how* this area was improving, I just celebrated that it was, and I was able to use the bathroom again without exertion. I also noticed a visible, gradual reduction of the bulge in and around my gut area as the days passed.

Was the mass shrinking? Surely not... Not already.

Could it?

Simultaneous to these developments, there was a subtle, almost intangible buoyancy or vibrancy throughout my tissues that I hadn't felt for so long that I almost forgot what it had felt like. Try as I may to describe it now, the change is almost something you must go through and feel for yourself in order to fully understand the degree in which it influences every move you make: taking in a breath, reaching for a glass of water, scratching an itch on the back of your neck, turning your head quickly when someone walks into a room, laughing when someone tells a funny joke...just the "stuff" you tell your body to do all the time but never think twice about. All of these regular, everyday physical actions that we take for granted when we're healthy receive a major blow when a person starts chemotherapy. Those medications bring about immeasurable side effects that no doctor knows how to warn a patient about, and no patient can prepare for. It just slows *everything* down and adds an element of raw, tender soreness to so many menial activities that one could never identify or list them all. That is, until they are lost and regained. Then, suddenly, the smallest motions accomplished without sharp shooting pains, aches, or that "creaky bones fatigue" is a breath of fresh air.

But, *again*, that didn't necessarily mean the natural protocol was working or healing me yet. I wanted to think that's where it was coming from, but the slight pep that was returning to me could have just been because I went off chemotherapy. In the same moment I was thanking God and my lucky stars that I was starting to feel more like my old self again, cancer could have been springing to life and spreading all over at a rapid pace.

Best not jump to conclusions.

I also noticed my sense of taste returning after a while. When I took a bite of a banana, I was tasting banana again, not solidified air. When I sipped on a smoothie, or crunched on a fresh salad, I could taste the flavors of blended fruits, vitamin-rich vegetables, and snappy, water-crisp lettuce again, as opposed to...well, *socks*. Wow. It's amazing how rarely it occurs to us to thank God for designing us with these little miracles called "taste buds" so we can enjoy the life-giving process of taking in nutrition and sustenance. That is until they fail. Then, suddenly, they are an inconceivable loss we don't know how to live without. So, when they come back, like they did in my case, every pop of flavor on the tongue is a "Hallelujah Chorus" just waiting to be sung. God really did make the world organically delicious.

For sure, though, losing your sense of taste is a side effect of chemotherapy, so getting it back didn't need to mean anything about the efficacy of my natural trifecta. Some of these wonderful improvements might just be side effects of going off one thing—not necessarily starting the other. Discontinuing the toxic chemotherapy was absolutely going to make me feel better. That's a "duh." Cancer, on the other hand, could be spreading by the second without that chemo mitigating the incoming toxins.

Oh yeah, and speaking of incoming toxins and organically delicious, it was around this time that I officially accepted pesticides as the lead culprit behind my cancer. Honestly, and as God is my witness, I really did eat *so* healthy before I got sick, and the rest of my lifestyle choices—embracing self-discipline and rejecting bad habits—supported the idea that I would never be a candidate for cancer. I was never exposed to toxic environments. It never ran in my family. There was literally no explanation, ever, as to why I developed it, let alone how it got so bad so fast that it nearly killed me overnight. But the one guilty pleasure in my life was fruits and vegetables, and I was not in the market for organic produce until this season of horror rained down upon me and I chose to commit forever to pesticide-free nutrition. And, as an interesting sidebar, as soon as I switched to a strictly organic diet, I decided to give some meat proteins a try again. The headaches of my youth that led me to becoming a reluctant vegetarian never came back. I was learning that I could eat meat, nuts, and produce without fear of migraines, cancer, or any other negative side effects as long as I just ate *clean*!

And now that I could spend a little extra physical exertion as my strength was just starting to come back to me, I began, one by one, implementing habits into my daily routine that I hadn't prioritized before, such as: stretching my whole body before getting out of bed to kickstart proper circulation; acquiring at least one half-hour per day of direct sunlight on my skin for optimum natural vitamin D production (as well as a long list of other benefits, like supporting bone health, keeping blood pressure in balance, killing invisible bacteria on and near the surface of the skin, increasing immunity, and boosting ones mood and psychological health); walking for at least a few minutes outside with my bare feet on the ground (called "earthing" or "grounding") to reduce inflammation, increase red blood cells, assist with balance, and lower harmful electromagnetic fields (EMFs) accumulated within the body, among other benefits; growing a vegetable or three, both for the nutritional benefit and the exercise (I still couldn't "exercise" in the traditional sense this early on in the transition, but, you know, a cherry tomato once in a while…); beginning my intermittent fasting routine every day at seven o'clock in the evening, which allows the liver to properly detox while my whole system rests from food consumption; and drink a lot—*a loooot*—of water throughout the day, capping each evening with a full eight hours of sleep.

Perhaps my favorite update of all from this time: I got to see my pal Neo again. Of course, we weren't out wrestling around as fiercely as the good old days, but for the first time since he had become my daily cancer-sniffing canine months back, I could talk to him, pat his little head, and take a few steps around the yard with him. What a good and faithful dog.

Neo and me, April 2022, only a few months after switching to the natural protocol

Little by little and day by day, I was becoming a tougher, stouter *me* again. Fearful Lynette—the inner voice of fear that had come preinstalled with the sinful condition I was born into (and who sometimes thinks she's in control)—had been silent for some time, and my prayers were becoming so different than they used to be. (I'll tell you one thing about being this miserable, Readers. Assuming you don't turn your back on God, which is the fastest route you can take to missing out on growth and blessings, seasons like these will teach you how to pray!) Maybe it was because this world spoke irreversible death over me, and God completely disregarded that dark promise, telling me through Cislyn that He still held the end of my story in His hands. Maybe it was because I didn't know what I had until I lost it all and, now, every moment was precious. Maybe it's because I had always appreciated the gift of life, family, love, laughter, and nature, and now I could officially say I have experienced everything in this list and a million other items with a richness I wouldn't have been capable of feeling prior to watching them almost float away. I'm sure it's all these contributing factors alongside many others that will take most of my life to identify, but my prayers will never be the same. I go well out of my way to specifically thank the Lord for a list of things that now mean so much to me I could cry just thinking about them…

Including my health—whatever amount I still had of it.

Now we just had to wait and see whether the doctors and their high-tech equipment agreed with the risky decisions I had made. Sure, I was feeling a little better, but I was also "feeling just fine" that day I went to urgent care: pre-chemotherapy but post-spread of cancer. It was all throughout me, and I didn't even know. If I had learned anything from that experience it was that the spread of cancer on the *inside* of the body didn't always have anything to do with how well or poor a person feels on any given day.

Would water, sunshine, and natural plants from the earth restore this body that God designed to self-heal in the first place? Or would these "dangerous" natural-healing methods be the death of me, like so many "doctors" online were claiming while they vociferously demanded the removal of videos, articles, blogs, and other forms of online presentations endorsing mushrooms, leaves, and seeds?

Only time would tell…and time was one thing I had in abundance.

Meanwhile, I knew, with the deepest assurance, that I had obeyed God. The only thing left to do was watch to see what God did with that radical act of obedience.

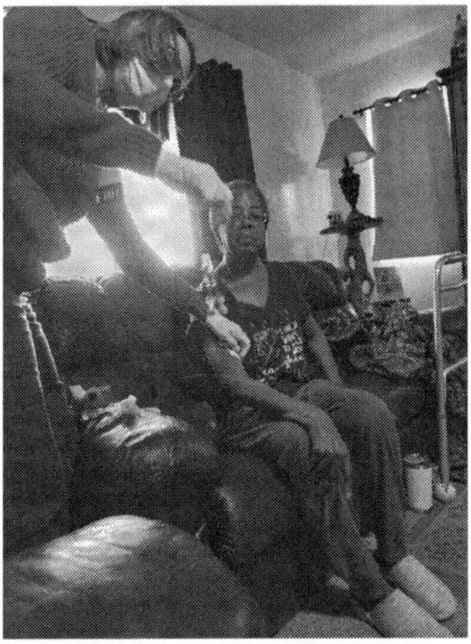

January 2022, just days into the new protocol—my walker for physical therapy is off to the right

Two months later, March 2022, in the final phases of physical therapy; my foster son of many years, pictured here, cried tears of joy and relief seeing me in person for the first time since I had returned home

Two more months later, May 2022, five months on natural protocol and beginning to finally put on a little weight; pictured with my grandson and his girlfriend

Also in May, standing tilted with my son, Adam, who held me up for a photo while my strength was still returning

Chapter Eighteen

"WHATEVER YOU'RE DOING... KEEP DOING IT"

It had now been just over a year and a half since that fateful phone call from Dr. Bakir interrupted my *Matrix* movie night with John back in July of 2021. Since then, I had experienced almost every extreme—upward climbs and downward plunges on the cancerous roller coaster without a break during the craziest and most confusing ride life could ever take anyone on. I've lost count of how many times I was jerked one direction and jolted another, over and again, but I will always clearly recall the sting of emotional whiplash when I think back over a few key moments...

As a quick, nutshell recap: The announcement—"I'm sorry to tell you, but you have cancer"—came out of nowhere following an appointment at an urgent care clinic because I had a "fiber deficiency." Within days, I had ovarian cancer that was *really* breast cancer and the bleak prognosis was that "stage four is incurable, and the cancer has spread *everywhere*," so I had "only months to live," during which time there was nothing anyone could do except "keep me comfortable until the end." And while I only had "months" to live, it took *more than* "months" (literally) to get the diagnosis, biopsies, insurance, and chemotherapy all sorted out and finally begin treatment. Depending on who you talk to, I was due to die before insurance ever kicked in, but I didn't. This showed me that God had wanted me to survive, come what may, despite all odds or human-originated predictions of lifespan. When the side effects of chemotherapy hit me, I felt like I was dying and doubt set in again, but Cislyn received a word from the Lord, speaking life into me and assuring me that He was "going to" touch me and heal me. My faith was restored and, though my physical health was in poor shape, my spiritual health was well above the ninth cloud while I believed I had a lot of years ahead of me—it was *not my time* to die!

Then I died.

...Yep. That happened.

Then, minutes afterward, I *un-died*, awakening into a scene out of the *Twilight Zone*: isolated, paralyzed, and in a hospital setting so foreign, unreal, and scary that I didn't even know whether I should engage with the hazmat-suited, masked strangers tending to my most intimate needs or leave them alone. Following this intense separation from my family over the family-gathering called Thanksgiving, I went home determined to do whatever necessary to beat this disease...and then God led me to stop the medicine designed to beat this disease.

Whiplash. Back and forth, back and forth. Every day was Opposite Day.

Would this frigid day in February, 2023—one year and one month from the date I cold-turkey-stopped my chemotherapy—be a good follow up or another death sentence? There was truly no way to tell. I really did trust God to carry me through all of this, place me in front of those I was supposed to reach through my testimony, and preserve my life up to the moment *He* chose to take me home (and not a second before). But, the last year and a half of my life had brought about so many bewildering twists and turns, taking me down paths I wouldn't have known to expect or plan for ahead of time, and with this hindsight firmly established, I now knew I couldn't assume *anything* about what my doctor might see on a scan.

February in the Fresno area of California is probably laughably warm to a lot of folks. With lows around 42 degrees, I'm sure I looked pretty silly walking under sunlit palm trees in a long, black winter coat, full-length scarf, and knit beanie cap, but I wasn't the only one. Maybe it was because so many of the patients and patrons of the cancer center had, like myself, just faced a season of tremendous physical weakness, and "chilly" for others was "freezing" for us while our bodies fought to regain strength. But whatever the cause may have been, lots of folks were bundled up just like I was. The "luxury resort" feel of this clinic's front hall had taken on an added "ski resort" feel from all the heavy coats and hats coming in and out the main entrance. In light of zero snow anywhere and sunshine as far as the eye could see, that contrast might have been comical if humor was a welcome visitor here. On the other hand, one never knew what these people were going through, what news they had just received, how they truly felt behind the courtesy smiles they wore, how much extra shivering they had faced in the last few weeks while their weight plummeted and they couldn't keep food down...and for that reason and so many others, I decided it would probably be best to not joke about scarves and winter hats. Polite smiles and nods would have to suffice as usual.

After signing in at the welcome desk, I took a seat and waited for my name to be called. Though I intentionally kept to myself so it wouldn't look as though I was rudely gawking at the other patrons, I couldn't help but feel extra aware of the people around me that day. In one sense, I had everything in common with all of them. Cancer is such an unbelievable experience that facing it has the power to pull even sworn enemies into a lasting, supportive friendship. Regardless of where we were all at in the various stages of treatment, everyone in that waiting room had either *already gone through* cancer's brand of hell on earth, and therefore had endless compassion and wonderful advice on how to get through it, or they were *about to face* cancerous hell on earth and had questions for the rest of us. Either way, we were certainly a family of sorts. Cancer is not a respecter of persons. It doesn't target people of one race, gender, religion, or culture over any other; it is proud to be an equal-opportunity destroyer-of-lives. Under normal social circumstances, a black, Christian female like me may find it a challenge to strike up a comfortable conversation with someone of another race, religion, or background, but in *this* waiting room, all the walls between people came down as everyone was a brother, sister, father, mother, son, or daughter to the next person over.

Then again, on this particular day, I was keeping a holistic, naturopathic, anti-chemo secret from my cancer family that made me feel slightly orphaned from the rest of them. Actually, I was keeping that secret from *everyone* in my life, including my husband. If I could completely present my case with all the details preserved just as they had played out in my journey—including the spiritual *and* logical justifications behind why I went off all Western care and relied solely on the medicines God instilled within the soil of the earth—one or two might applaud me and seek my advice, but there was no doubt in my mind that the vast majority of these cancer-center patrons would write me off as a nut-job. Who in their right mind would ever *dare* stop chemotherapy overnight for seeds and tea?

I can hear the answer from most lips right now: "Someone with a death wish; *that's* who."

Yeah... Today was different. These were still my brothers and sisters, but if they only knew my secret, I would be the black sheep of this community who turned my back on the medicine that united us all. I would be branded as the one who had taken a divergent path, strayed in another direction, and forsaken the chemo-gold of the fold.

I would be "crazy."

Well, "crazy," sure. But...would I be *right*?

Had I truly heard correctly from the Lord? I mean, it was such an incredibly radical idea to discontinue the only medication considered to be the sovereign treatment for this fatal/terminal condition. Absolutely everything in society and culture had so long preached that a person who stops chemotherapy before he or she is told to is a person who stops living before his or her truly appointed time. It's cut-and-dry simplicity at its finest: Taking these pills is your only chance to live; not taking these pills is certain death. The choice is yours.

And the choice *was* mine; I made it, and I stood behind it. The only question now was whether I had made the right one.

Of course, I knew I had, because it was God's plan, but the absolute, irrefutable proof remained to be seen for certain in today's pudding. Luckily, scans are not biased to whether people follow their gut, their heart, their God or gods, or their doctor; they're just images reporting what's inside the body...like those from the appointment I had the previous August when I had reported for a routine visit with Dr. Ibrahim in summer of 2022. By that time, I had already been off chemotherapy for seven months. I was *open to* a miracle of God, but I wouldn't let myself expect too much so soon. Sure, testimonials online sounded really amazing and quick for some who dared to go against the system, but *I* was the whiplash woman. *I* was the woman who would never die, then had months to live, then would never die again, then died, then came back to life and almost died forty more times. Who was I to have any expectations whatsoever regarding the results of a seven-months-post-chemo imaging session?

Readers, you can't even imagine how shocked I was in that moment she walked in and told me the twelve-centimeter mass was *gone*. As in, disappeared. Not "in the process of leaving," not "shrinking and we'll keep our fingers crossed," just twelve full, cancerous centimeters of disease-lump vanished entirely like it was never there. Her exact words were: "The MRI machine was hard-pressed to find that tumor of yours."

Hair growing back in August of 2022—the same month I was told the mass was gone

Wearing a wig around the same time; only about six months on the natural protocol, my face was already radiating health again!

Did that really just happen? Had I heard her correctly?

Certainly, I felt all the good things you're supposed to feel—happiness, amazement, relief—but I didn't allow myself to take the celebration *too* far because technically, I still had cancer elsewhere throughout my body. I also chose not to tell Dr. Ibrahim that I had discontinued my oral chemo pills. I didn't want to defend or explain myself to one as well-versed in cancer treatments as she. Even though my journey was a prayerful one involving many sober and mature conversations with God, no matter what I told her, I knew I would come across as impulsive and reckless. I also knew in advance that I would receive dire warnings from her about how the cancer, mass and all, would return full-swing and eat me alive in a matter of months—warnings that honestly wouldn't have changed anything about what I had decided to do in obedience to God, though it *would* serve to introduce a fresh loop of fear and uncertainty…so I simply stayed the natural course, kept it all to myself, and looked forward to seeing what the next scan would show, praying that it, too, would display a little cancer-eradication progress.

Now, another half-year had passed, and I was right back in the same waiting room to go over the latest pictures...

Would this natural healing method be confirmed *again* with today's full-body follow-up scan? Would some of that black-blob-on-black-blob nonsense I'd seen before be a little lighter this time? Was I about to observe with my own eyes the fruits of obedience to God manifested into a few restored tissues?

...Or was I about to see frightening proof that God's plan was more complicated and confusing than I had thought, and I was a grand misinterpreter of His directives?

"Lynette Hill?" a medical assistant called from the doorway.

It was time to find out...

Minutes later, I was sitting in Dr. Ibrahim's usual consultation office, fighting the temptation to bite my nails again. I was a spaghetti of confidence and nerves at the same time: I just *knew* that God would bless me for faithfully following His prompt to go completely natural...so I was "calm." I "had this." Those images were going to look better than last time, and before I left this office today, I was going to hear my doctor say that I just might have a chance at life again. I just *knew* it.

But what if I was wrong, and the cancer was—like Dr. Ibrahim would have predicted last August if she had known I stopped chemo—back full-swing, but even worse than before? Sure, I felt stronger now, leaving the house alone, driving about, having some independence returned to me, and walking as if there was never even a question of neuropathy or a potentially wheelchair-bound life, but what if that was only temporary? What if the *true* "last word" on the subject of chemotherapy vs. God's handiwork was that I made a stupid mistake, misunderstood something God was trying to tell me, went off the good stuff, and signed my own death certificate? Was my own life about to become the payment for an imprudent error?

Stop it, I chided Fearful Lynette. *We've been over this eight billion times. God spoke, I listened, and this report is going to show the miraculous result of that simple combination.*

With a deep breath, I closed my eyes and offered up a prayer from my heart to the Lord, whom I believed had already won this cancer battle on my behalf. I opened my eyes once more at the sound of the light click from the doorknob. When the door swung open and Dr. Ibrahim slipped in, I thought I caught a glimmer of a smile under her COVID-19 mask—an expression of gladness made known by the way her eyes lifted at the edges.

She looks happy. I bet it's good news.

"Hellooooo!" my oncologist sang out, offering her hand in greeting.

She sounds happy, too. This looks promising.

Everyone in this building always looks happy, Fearful Lynette retorted.

It had been some time since I had heard my inner fear spring up, but so many rumors about chemotherapy say that if you go off your medication, you'll feel better in the beginning, but the cancer will suddenly come back and take over your body rapidly months later. I felt amazing, but if the cancer was going to come bounding back with a vengeance, the time would put that...right about now.

It's a cancer center. Doctors who come across unhappy or depressed with their patients wouldn't have a job here for long. It doesn't mean anything for you. You foolishly discontinued the very medicine that would have given you good results today. I bet your scans are so black that even the experts can't make heads or tails of them.

No, Faithful Lynette said with calm assurance. *I heard from God, and I did the right thing. He's going to honor that. Just watch...*

I quickly shook Dr. Ibrahim's hand, a little perkier than normal, and then straightened my posture as one who is alert and ready for a meeting of minds, quickly lacing my fingers together over my knees. Yes, in part, my upbeat movements were because I was feeling stronger, but more accurately, I was just anxious for her to get straight to it.

Hurry up! Tell me already!

"You look like you're feeling amazing," Dr. Ibrahim said, settling into her swivel chair and adjusting the monitor.

"I *am* feeling amazing!" I confirmed.

While she clicked around, opened some files, typed in a password or two, and prepared to give me the latest imaging results, we traded some casual chitchat about the cold weather, and it came up that I was once again out and about town alone. There was a day—and not that long before this one, to tell the truth—that neither of us thought I would ever be strong enough to walk, drive, or even sit up straight again. Yet, here I was, looking and feeling like a million bucks and praying the MRI results followed suit.

Please doc! I begged silently. *Please give me good news!*

They were the same words I repeated in my head the night Dr. Bakir called to tell me what the "blood abnormality" was all about. And now, I had come full circle. Here I was, again, *possibly* on the other side of a journey, pleading in identical terms.

This time, Dr. Ibrahim didn't have pictures to show me. Instead, she pulled up a list of notes compiled between her and the radiologist, but she didn't bother adjusting the monitor toward me so I could read them, likely because I wouldn't have known what I was looking at anyway.

No pictures of black blobs? Maybe that means the blobs shrank a little? Faithful Lynette pondered hopefully.

It means there hasn't been any change, you idiot, Fearful Lynette jabbed. *She doesn't have anything to show you because there's nothing new to report. You're lucky you're even alive right now. When this appointment is over you should probably go home and swallow some of that chemo you've been hiding in your closet for over a year.*

You're wrong, said Faithful Lynette. *Look. She's shaking her head and smiling. Please, God, PLEASE let this be good news! Tell me the cancer has started to diminish, even a little—the tiniest bit of progress, I'll take it.*

Dr. Ibrahim's eyes darted here and there on the monitor while she covered the preliminary remarks for a good twenty seconds or so. I studied her expression as she described what it was like seeing the radiologist's report. As she geared up to deliver the meat of the update, she appeared to be pleasantly surprised and excited.

"I have to admit, I wasn't expecting this at all," she said, releasing a small, bubbly, but subtle laugh.

Was that a chuckle I just heard? Faithful Lynette asked. *Did she seriously just chuckle? This sounds like really, REALLY good news. Come on, come on! The suspense is killing me!*

"I'm impressed," Dr. Ibrahim finally concluded. "I couldn't be happier with these results. Other than chemotherapy, I don't know what you're doing, but whatever it is, keep doing it." She turned away from the monitor, rolled her chair closer to me, leaned forward, clasped her hands together, looked me directly in the eye, and, in a tone as serious as a heart attack, spoke a sentence I never thought I would hear and will never forget as long as I live…

"You have *no* cancer activity in your body."

"Praise the Lord!" I yelled instantly and at full volume. The words exploded out of me *so* fast, they had already started clamoring down the nearby hallways in all directions before it even occurred to me I had spoken aloud.

If every hope I had dared to hope—if every prayer I had dared to pray in this past year and a half—could have been compiled and crunched together into the grandest of all optimistic expectations, I still wouldn't have anticipated hearing "*no* cancer activity." I would have been as happy as a clam on a pile of salt *just* to hear that my condition hadn't worsened. I would have broken into a solo-round of the Wah-Watusi dance *just* to learn that one or two of those black blobs of death was showing signs of shrinkage around the edge. And if Dr. Ibrahim had told me that the "cancer-free" label was even a possibility—even the remotest prospect; even an eventual goal for *years* down the road—I would have shouted for joy, because that would have been enough to illustrate that God's plan really was and *is* a reasonable, sensible alternative to Western meds. It would prove, once and for all, to *me* if not to everyone else, that I wasn't "crazy" after all for believing: a) God's plants would treat my flesh more gently than the toxins in chemotherapy while still effectively and aggressively killing cancer cells; b) God's voice and directives can be trusted, even when they radically go against the grain or the societally championed narrative; c) what God made is always better than what *we* made; d) that He knew what He was doing when He provided the "herb for the service of man" (Psalm 104:14); and e) when He says He is "going to" touch and heal one of His children, then He is "going to," regardless of odds or evidence to the contrary.

All of these wonderful reflections could have easily been gleaned from a humble, meager recovery progress report.

But to hear that there was "no cancer" in my body?!

None *at all*?!

I didn't know what to do with myself. I didn't know what to think, what to say, or how to respond to such an incredible update. Other than perhaps the birth of my children, the day I married John, and the moment I truly accepted Jesus as my Savior, this was *the* biggest moment in my life, and it was too much to take in and process. I felt like running, leaping, screaming, flailing…I felt like *exploding* into outbursts of praise and gladness and forcing the entire building to celebrate right along with me. I wanted to set fire to the invisible ethics-sign that says, "Quiet zone: Sad people nearby—this is not the time or place to rejoice." I wanted to hunt down the spirit of depression and death so heavy in this cancer center, punch it in the face, throttle it by the neck, and then throw it off the balcony in front of hundreds of terminal patients to the sound of their uproarious applause. I wanted to disintegrate the fear and anxiety that pulsated within these walls and replace it with promises of future health, long lifespans, hopes and dreams, vitality, love, and… *joy*—that ever-elusive emotion so many of these precious folks hadn't felt in so long.

I wanted *everybody* to feel what I was feeling…

…And to know what I now knew about this hush-hush enterprise the world called "alternative medicine."

Gasp. Wait. Hold up.

Had I just found my calling? Did I just identify perhaps why God allowed me to go through all of this—to tell everyone *about* all of this?

Readers, can you even imagine what might happen if the whole world knew about the healing power of these plant-based, all-natural medicines God made with His own hands? The very thought that I might be able to truly help someone in the same or similar *horrible* position I had been in over the past year made my insides burst with happiness and gratitude, and it clearly showed on the outside… I was smiling larger than the grandest boomerang from the Land Down Under.

Dr. Ibrahim's smile matched my own. No COVID-19 mask on the planet had the power of concealing that celebratory expression of hers. It was so wide, it threatened to tear straight through the thin paper.

"This is *amazing* news, Doctor," I said, battling to contain myself. "This is just so…*big*! It's huge!"

"Yes," she agreed. "I am so happy with your progress and how you're doing! Like I said, *whatever* you're doing, keep it up. It's working!"

If only she knew what really led to these cancer-free scans, I thought. *I honestly don't think she would even believe me. I don't think anyone would.*

Well, John would have believed me. And Laura would have as well. But my near-death experience through Thanksgiving of 2021 was still so fresh on everyone's minds that I wanted to get as much space as possible between now and that horrible season before I told them everything. In the meantime, however, I did have an incredible update to share.

I'll never forget when I called John from the car after that appointment. What a moment of pure joy we shared in celebration together. It was such a feast of gladness after so much sadness had hit our world in the last couple years.

"What?! Wait a minute... Say that again," John said with an ecstatic tone.

"I'm tellin' you honey! She looked at her monitor thing, shook her head, and she was kinda smiling, you know, like, looking all excited, and she said my scans were clear and I was cancer-free!"

"That's what she said? You're sure?" After hesitating a moment, he made me tell him the whole story again, and I was happy to oblige. I raced through an abbreviated version of the details of that morning's appointment, landing on the same conclusion.

"...and that's when she said, 'Lynette, whatever you're doing, keep it up, because it's working. There is no cancer activity in your body anywhere!' and I shouted, 'Praise the Lord!'"

"There's *no way* you could have misunderstood her, though?" John checked again before throwing his worry to the wind.

For *a third time* in a row—though I was happy to revisit the refreshingly good news as many times as he needed—I gave John the breakdown of that morning and Dr. Ibrahim's words. "I have 'no cancer activity in my body,' John!"

"Wow. Cancer-free..." John couldn't believe it. He had his own hard, dark hours of self-reflection and having to come to grips with the possibility of losing me. The worst of all would always be that particularly disturbing moment when they carted me off to ICU to resuscitate me. That was when Dr. Ibrahim told him he couldn't go with me and I probably wasn't coming home. What a scary, vulnerable time that was... It was no wonder he had to hear the amazing news three times before it would sink in.

My family surrounding me on Thanksgiving, 2022—
one year exactly from the *Twilight Zone* Thanksgiving I spent alone
and only eleven months from the start of the natural protocol

When the timing was right, I would tell John, Laura, my doctors, and then the *world*—in that order—about my chemo-free secret. We were getting closer to that time by the day, but I still wanted to pray about it a while. I didn't want to bombard anyone close to me with something they would interpret *on their end* to be a fast-track path to death, like going off chemotherapy before I was instructed to. The roller-coaster was just too hard to ride a second time. And if Laura and John didn't even know yet, Dr. Ibrahim wouldn't, as my husband and sister would naturally be the first to receive such major news.

Thankfully, I wasn't under any obligation to tell Dr. Ibrahim, or anyone else, what changes I had made to my treatment. And although the discovery that cancer was no longer active within my body due to natural methods was an enormous development worthy of being heralded from every rooftop in the world, I needed to *stay* cancer-free for a while before I took this groundbreaking knowledge to the airways. Meanwhile, Faithful Lynette was erupting into so many praises at once that it would be impossible to isolate just one. She was bursting like a good-feelings piñata hit by a freight train, while Fearful Lynette was, once again, silenced…maybe for good this time. My inner fear had been wrong so many times in a row lately and it was starting to feel good being so confident in my faith and my ability to hear the voice of God.

My Heavenly Father had certainly been speaking to me a lot lately, and in His own gentle way, He had told me: The day was coming that I would get my story in some form of media (video, book, article, blog, or something to that effect) and spread the word about *His* meds to whatever online audience would hear me. On my end, I didn't care if that was five people or five billion people. God was preparing me to raise awareness about this topic for the benefit of His children, and my job was to speak, while His job was to carry what I spoke to those He knew needed to receive it. That much of the arrangement was a done deal, and I had sensed it for a long time now, but something about the way this appointment had just gone down made it all "click" within me on another level. It wasn't just that I would be asked to "go and tell," Great-Commission-style, about my healing; it was my *calling*. Almost something I had been born into this world to do. It was going to be huge!

However, the timing needed to be considered carefully…

It seemed a risk either way: Speak too soon and risk the cancer coming back, or speak too late and risk missing the opportunity to reach those desperate people who would have found my story earlier on. Either way, one thing was proving more certain in this modern world than anything else: Once I posted something online and it got any level of attention, there would be no taking it down. There is no such thing as un-saying something that floated throughout the globe to hundreds, thousands, or even millions of peoples' screens. Even taking it down wouldn't matter by then. Consider the uncountable times someone has put something online and the world's response is to download it and re-post it from secondary media accounts. It happens with generally everything nowadays, and I would be naïve to think it wouldn't happen to me.

And seriously, let's be real: Who could blame them? My claims were fundamentally radical and countercultural, as well as revolutionary and sensational! This was big news! That a person could avoid the side effects of chemotherapy and still receive effective treatment for their cancer was already an astounding assertion. That they could do so for less than pennies on the dollar cost when comparing Western to natural methods was likewise shocking. That they might not only live but soar into new seasons of longevity and prosperity via swallowing the medicine the Creator of the universe personally whipped up for them was so extraordinary it bordered on being unbelievable! There was no doubt about it: The day I came out and boldly claimed all of *those* things, it was going to ignite an explosion with permanent, irreversible ripples.

When God chose to attract the eyes and ears of people all over the world with my video, blog, article, or book, there would be no going back, so I needed to be absolutely sure He had given me the green light to speak.

All in His timing. Right?

Little did I know in that moment, the voice of God was about to tell me to take this groundbreaking news to the airwaves sooner than I thought.

June 2023—
John was so happy to get his wife back!

Chapter Nineteen

THE RIGHT KIND OF VIRAL

"...But, aside from all of that, this is even more important than the things I just mentioned about what I ingest in my body: Your mind is *the* most important thing. The Bible says, 'life and death is in the power of the tongue,' so as hard as it is, don't focus on your cancer."

It was good advice, sure. And some might even say "important advice." A flatterer would insist it was "crucial." But the numbers just didn't add up: My very first natural health testimony on TikTok had received more than a *million* views in a single night, soaring well beyond my grandest expectations.

"Focus on life. Speak *life* to yourself, every day. Look in the mirror and say, 'I am cancer-free. I am going to live a long and healthy life.'"

It was completely unscripted. I spoke as casually as anyone else staring into a phone from a patio bounce-rocker on their front lawn. I wasn't pounding pulpits, pumping fists in the air, raising my voice, or delivering powerful, "keynote speaker at a conference" articulations in front of a slide show... But, for some reason—some God-only-knows reason (literally)—in less than twenty-four hours, my first video about natural healing methods for cancer was gearing up to be as viral as anything else that had ever broken the Internet.

I was right to be concerned about the timing, and to be certain it was God who told me to proceed before I posted anything. And wow... When *He* green-lights a project, you can expect it to make waves.

I remember the first time I uploaded the video, which was a different platform at that time, it was taken down instantly for "medical disinformation." I wasn't too discouraged. In fact, a part of me wondered if I would receive the same kind of blocking, shadow-banning, and rejection as all the other pro-natural presenters online who had helped me get off chemotherapy. Sure enough, my own natural healing content offended the first video-sharing website so much I was kicked to the curb within hours of posting. Without taking it personally, I shrugged and simply re-posted it to a second online media platform, but the result was the same as the first. By that point, I had enough hours in prayer and seeking the Lord's will to know that two dismissals didn't amount to anything, so I went for another round, loading my super-casual, nonchalant, five-minute opinion-piece on TikTok. My hope was *only* that I would find it still up and available to the public after my morning rounds the following day. Under no circumstances did I anticipate seeing a large number of views had transpired throughout the night. Ten views would have been neat. Twenty-five would have been cool. Maybe, if all my friends and family had been paying close attention to what I did online, I might get *really* lucky and see them all support me at the same time, driving the counter to forty or fifty views.

When I checked the following day, my video was still up, the counter was ticking by the second, and more than *one million people* had already watched and listened to what I had to say regarding naturopathic ingredients from the soil, their efficacy in fighting cancer, and the power of the tongue to speak life. It was clear that God wanted *His* medicine represented online, and from more than just a few timid articles that drop toxicity warnings and wrap it all in the term "alternative medicine."

Let me be clear: there is nothing "alternative" about God's medicine. The ingredients that healed *me* are those that the Creator of the entire universe put on this planet from the beginning with the intention of keeping His children alive and thriving. If anything, it's the current mainstream, manmade, laboratory-enhanced Western protocol that would more appropriately be called "alternative," at least based on how unnatural and poisonous it is to the human body—and it *most definitely should* be that system that earns the toxicity warnings. (Ask someone who knows. Chemotherapy is hell on earth. There's no doubt it's a ravenous and destructive venom, especially when even your own gentle, cautious, and diplomatic oncologist warns you several times that it's "brutal"—with heavy emphasis on the word.)

Needless to say, my husband John and sister Laura were going to hear about this video of mine that went viral overnight. Soon after its TikTok debut, they caught wind of it and…it eventually came around to an awkward and very pointed question.

"I saw your video, and I think it's great how many others have seen it," John said at first. "But I noticed—"

Uh oh, I thought warily. *Here we go.*

"Why didn't you give chemotherapy any credit for your healing?" Laura asked.

Laura, who, aside from John, had been my closest medical advocate at home during this entire journey, was eyeing me with hesitation. I knew it was time. If the both of them *were* still inclined to feel frightened and vulnerable in discovering I discontinued the very medicine doctors were calling my only chance, I couldn't protect them from those feelings any longer. I saw it coming that John was about to get very direct…and then he did.

"You *are* still using your medications, right?"

I looked him in the eye, almost apologetically, and blurted it all out in one fell swoop to spare us both a lot of dancing around the proverbial bush.

"Honey, I haven't taken chemotherapy in over a year."

John's face took on an ashen-white tone as his mouth fell open in shock. "You… You were…" He swallowed and tried again. "You were healed by the *natural* things you were taking, and *only* those?"

I nodded, feeling both guilt for having kept the secret this long and relief that it was finally out of the bag. "Yeah. Just soursop tea, black seed oil, apricot kernels, and the rest of my natural routine and regimen. Actually, Laura," I said turning to my precious sibling, "chemotherapy was cut from my protocol completely on January first, 2022. I have not touched it since, other than to stash it away in my closet."

From left: me, my mother, and Laura, one year after I discontinued chemotherapy

I went on to explain: I had not processed refills on any of the other Western prescriptions—including a hormone blocker the experts had me on that specifically warns consumers it may "lead to cancer." Meanwhile, I didn't know how or when to tell my family, but I wanted the timing to be right because I didn't want them to worry *or* try to talk me off my course. I never once lied to John, Laura, or anyone else about whether I was taking my pills, but nobody had asked directly until now. And, now that they had, I couldn't lie. "I really feel it's what God asked me to do," I said, praying they would understand.

The shock in John's features resembled how they looked the night Dr. Bakir announced my cancer, except, this time, it was amazement instead of pure terror.

"You are the bravest person I know," John said lovingly. "I could not do that!"

That was sweet of him to say, but who knows? Maybe that's *just* what he would have done if he would have heard petrifying terms like "stage four," "incurable," and "months to live"—all while watching people online run across stages in front of live audiences miraculously healed and cancer-free for five straight years on nothing more than leaves, seeds, and oils…? Maybe it's what Laura would have done, too?

"Okay, Lynette," Laura uttered in a shaky, emotional tone. "As a… As a nurse, I *cannot* advise you to make this decision and to do what you've done."

It was not a time to interrupt. If anything, having been by my side through all of this, Laura had earned far more than the right to weigh in on my medical decisions as everything that happened to me affected her as well. I remained silent and receptive.

"But as your sister," she steadied herself with a deep breath, "as one who knows everything you went through, who saw you face all of that, I am so proud of you."

Proud of me?

Now it was *me* who had to take a steadying breath. These words from John and Laura were a salve, spreading like a remedial honey over deep, itchy, festering wounds that had taken root within me during those countless hours alone in the hospital over Thanksgiving of 2021.

"You actually walk the walk and talk the talk," Laura added. "I say *I* have faith, but what you've done...you prove with your actions that *you* have faith! Faith in God, and in His ability to lead you. I'm serious, Lynette. I am *so* proud of you."

If only I had known back in those days, when the imaginary Rod Serling narrative over my life was my only constant, that I was going to make it home alive, radically change my cancer protocol, experience total restoration, and *then* hear John call me "brave" and Laura say she's "proud"...

What swelled within me in that moment was enough to heal more than just cancer. I was whole again: physically, spiritually, emotionally, and mentally. God didn't only lead me down a path of restoration for the body, alone, but for a whole-person, holistic, head-to-toe, heart-and-soul *renewal.* Even my doctors were compelled to admit that what happened with me defied everything they had been taught to expect from science and medicine.

Was it perhaps because they had witnessed something more than merely "Western vs. natural"? Had they maybe—just maybe—witnessed something even *supernatural?* Their reactions appeared to suggest as much.

About three months after breaking the news to John and Laura, I attended one of my routine monthly follow-ups with my primary, Dr. Bakir. He was all smiles and nothing but smiles as I sat there with my working legs, my growing hair in a thick braid around my face, my skin smooth and radiant, my eyes bright, and my belly flat.

"I know I am a scientist," Dr. Bakir said, alluding to a primarily secular worldview. "But, *you* are making me believe in miracles."

I smiled, resisting the urge to burst into a hearty "Hallelujah" on the spot.

"Based on your scans, and your diagnosis from last year," he shook his head with a smirk, "you should not be here. *Your scans are not the scans of someone that lives!*"

Even more telling than his reaction, however, was that of Dr. Ibrahim's. She, unlike Dr. Bakir, was a scientist and doctor specifically within the field of cancer, so she would have been the first between the two of them to present a perfectly reasonable explanation for something that *looked like* a miracle but was, in fact, a patient catching a lucky break somewhere in all that treatment chemistry. Try as she might to spot the fluke, however, at the end of the day, this cancer expert was as mystified as Dr. Bakir.

In December of 2023, when this very book was about half-written, I was lucky enough to connect with Dr. Ibrahim outside of her office. Up to that point, she still hadn't been provided a complete explanation of what changed within my treatment. In our most recent appointment, when we went over my labs again and they showed clear of cancer, I mentioned I hadn't been taking chemotherapy, but I didn't say how long that had been the case; nor did I divulge any of my natural healing protocol at that time. She acknowledged my statement only briefly, and then moved right along in the discussion of labs. It didn't come up again that day.

To my surprise, however, a few days later, she called me directly and asked if I would be willing to meet her for lunch, so we could "speak freely" about my situation. On my end, I was just happy to get together with a doctor who had only ever given me the kindest, most sincere and genuine care in my worst hours, primarily so I could thank her for all she had done for all of us. If I happened to be given an opportunity to pick her brain about natural healing, that would be a bonus, but it wasn't the central purpose behind our visit. I'm not certain exactly what the motive was on her end to meet me for lunch, but maybe it was so she could hear precisely what I had been up to when she had encouraged me: "Whatever it is you're doing, keep doing it, because it's working!" Regardless, we picked a date and time and I let her in on my secret as soon as the conversation presented a spontaneous opportunity.

"Let me ask you something," Dr. Ibrahim said, folding her hands together atop the table in front of her. "I have not had to renew a single prescription for you for a *long* time. In fact, the prescription for your oral chemotherapy ran out months ago. I expected your refill request to come in already, but I haven't heard a word. Did you make a request with the office? Or…?"

"Actually, I'm glad you brought that up, because there's something I wanted to tell you today." I adjusted my posture and got straight to the point: "I haven't asked for a refill because I haven't touched my chemotherapy in almost two years."

Dr. Ibrahim blinked once or twice, probably waiting for the "just kidding" punchline, and when it didn't come, her eyes widened in shock. Her brows lifted and her mouth opened slightly as her head dipped a few inches closer to me. Judging by her expression, she found the news to be inconceivable, but doubt and skepticism were completely missing from her face as well, so it appeared she believed me.

Feeling encouraged to continue, I proceeded to tell her everything I had done. I started from the beginning, giving her a truncated recapitulation of my return from the hospital in late 2021, the research I had done into the world of natural healing, the miraculous testimonies of those it had already worked for in recent years, all the videos and articles supporting my convictions, and finally, the ingredients I chose and how I had been taking them since. She never interrupted once. It was clear from her countenance she was hanging on my every word. When I had spilled it all, she gave an encouraging response...but I wondered if I was picking up on the slightest reservations in her tone.

"Well," she said cautiously, "looking at you today, it's obvious you're thriving. It *looks* like you made the right decision for you. I mean, this choice you've made... Wow, what a *brave* woman you are! I mean that was really, *really* brave."

I smiled in response, wondering if the gavel of Western warnings was getting ready to drop, but it never came. She was gracious and accepting of my story up to that point, clearly respecting me as an independent woman with convictions of my own. Our lunch had been beautiful, and I was fortunate enough to snag a selfie or two with her as we went our separate ways.

Between that pleasant departure and the day I found out what Dr. Ibrahim had really been thinking during that luncheon, I had an important imaging session to tend to. On January 19, 2024—less than two months ago at the time of this writing—I made a hefty donation to the medical community's "scans we can't explain" box...

My day started at six o'clock in the morning, when I slipped from my bed to the dresser drawers, and then to my closet to grab my clothes, all by the light of my cell phone so John could sleep. Minutes later, I stood in front of my bathroom mirror with my teeth brushed, face washed, and dressed in blue and black checkered pants with a black turtleneck—all-cotton attire appropriate for the PET (positron emission tomography) scan scheduled at seven sharp.

But there was something *more* in the reflection of that mirror than just a lady with coordinated clothing who was ready to meet another day. This day was paramount. Not too many months before, I had sat on the edge of the bathtub behind me and cried harder than I had ever cried in my life.

Look at you now, girl.

I couldn't be more proud of what God had done with what was once a hopeful, faithful, but unshaped and only partially tested lump of clay: molding and shaping me into *this*. It was a painful process, sure—involving some unfathomably hard days in the Potter's kiln, when I felt alone amidst the heat—but that's what the Potter does when the clay is willing. In the beginning, we are placed on a wheel and ceaselessly spun, enduring torrents of suffocating water as we're smashed and pulled repeatedly under the pressure of the initial sculpting. The Potter's wheel stops, and we're thrust into the furnace and fired. It's tempting in those moments to cry out, "Where are You, Lord?" But I happen to know that *my* God is a God who isn't afraid to stand in the hottest flames of the furnace right by our side (Daniel 3). Though it takes grit and determination to get through the process, *without it* we are doomed to remain weak, lumpy, useless, and filled with impurities. When we emerge from the kiln, however, we feel different; we *are something different*—a new creation, beautiful, useful, and pure. And it is then that we realize what a fearfully and wonderfully made vessel the Potter has formed us into (Psalm 139:14).

Look at what the Potter has done with you, Faithful Lynette said. *No longer a useless lump, you are an empowered, independent vessel...with the alligator-skin glaze.*

A smile crept across my face. Fearful Lynette was long gone. She had been silenced now for so long, I couldn't even remember the last time I was confronted by the voice of my own inner fear. This day would *not* be a day of worry and doubt. This day was a day when the Potter's vessel would storm the gates of the cancer center and show every last one of them the miracle that God's medicine had performed upon human flesh when nobody thought it was possible. I was certain of it—no doubt in my mind: The scans scheduled to take place in less than an hour were, in the spiritual realm, already done and clear.

It had been almost a year since Dr. Ibrahim had pronounced me cancer-free, and I hadn't changed anything about the protocol that healed me in the first place, so as far as God and I were concerned, the PET scan was merely a formality. However, it was a formality I was more than happy to carry out for the benefit of those who still needed another image, another picture, another bit of proof that this "silly, ill-advised, seeds-and-leaves protocol that crazy Lynette lady did" is actually worth taking a closer look at. I was willing to be under scrutiny so the Lord's protocol might earn more than an eye roll from the medical community. Sure! Why not?

Look at me! What a perfect candidate for such a thing!

It wasn't about being attractive, hot, sexy, or any of those temporal bragging rights. It was about being alive!

Look at the whites of those eyes... They're actually white! Not jaundice-yellow. Look at that hair regrowth, woven into a braid as valid a 'do on me as any proud woman in the black community. Oh, and those nails. I managed to get through this whole thing without giving into the temptation to bite them, and now they're long, natural, and pretty. That skin is velvety soft and a perfect chocolate brown—not scaley, flakey, or burned with dark spots like it was on chemotherapy. But more than anything else, look at that vitality. This face is not the face of a woman with cancer.

And it wasn't. My face had now become the face of a woman who *beat* cancer and lived to spread the word about how for the sake of other hurting people. I had—through a *hard* journey and a few viral videos—become one of the spokesmodels for God's protocol. When I was making my way through the valley of the shadow of death, I certainly did "feel" fear, as all humans do, but fear never owned me.

Now, here I was, on the other side of the journey, participating with the formalities to prove my Lazarus-come-forth moment was everything I said it was. As for whether or not I personally needed to see the scans, I didn't. I had already come out of the tomb and resurfaced to mingle about in the land of the living. Why? Because I was special? No; simply because my Lord had—like He had with Lazarus—called me out from the tomb. If everyone *else* needed a photo of the raised Lazarus, I would give them what they wanted, but it wasn't for *my* sake.

I look amazing today.

I feel amazing today.

And that's gonna show in my scans today.

As I quietly slipped past my sleeping John, I smiled yet again, remembering the night before. He had asked if I wanted him to go with me to this appointment, and I told him no. It was a happy moment for me on many levels. My independence and ability to drive myself around without any assistance from John had been the norm for a while, but it wasn't about whether it was "new." Now, it had become the gift I would never take for granted again: No, John didn't need to accompany me to speak with the doctor to hold my hand in case we received bad news; no, John didn't need to hold me around the waist and help me in and out of the car; no, John didn't need to drive in case I passed out from exhaustion.

Nope. This time, John could sleep in.

This was the life. I had it made…and in addition to every other wonderful thing that had put a pep in my step that day, I was going to receive the praise reports on those scans *much* faster than advertised.

They said Dr. Ibrahim would know the results of the scans by the following Tuesday afternoon, so I only had to wait through that evening, then the weekend, and then an additional day and a half from there before I could be certain. And that was alright. I could wait. I already knew what the results were going to be, anyway.

But then: At just after five o'clock in the early evening, the same day as the scan, my phone lit up with an app notification. The doctor/patient communication portal had just gone live with an update to my medical records: As God is my witness, it was the result of the PET scan from that morning: Not only was it clear—no trace of cancer anywhere in the body at all—it was *so* clear that the radiologist was able to read the images and produce an answer within a few hours, *much* faster than they anticipated.

For some reason, despite the wonderful (if unsurprising) update, Dr. Ibrahim wanted me to come in for an in-person follow up a week later, and now I'm glad I obliged. She didn't tell me anything I didn't already know, but as it turned out, that wasn't what I was supposed to get out of the visit, anyway.

"You know," Dr. Ibrahim said after the obvious results of the scans had been discussed, "when we shared lunch that day, I just *knew* your next scans were going to show that the cancer had come back full-swing. I just *knew* I was going to see it everywhere, all throughout your body, and worse than before."

So, *that's* what she had been thinking that day. Even though she was a hundred percent supportive and respectful, I sensed that she was holding something back. While she was sitting there across the table from me, nodding and smiling through my praise reports and testimonies of natural medicine, she was probably crying for me on the inside, believing I had signed my own death warrant. Poor Dr. Ibrahim. I didn't mean to put her in that position.

"Lynette, here's the deal," she went on. "Anytime a patient communicates to us that he or she plans to discontinue chemotherapy prematurely, we respond with a very serious, *critical* warning: If they discontinue the protocol before the designated window of treatment has come to an end, their cancer is *going to* come back within about three to six months. Trust me, as an oncologist, I've seen the pattern. And when the cancer inevitably does come back, it comes back multiple times worse. At that time, there simply won't be anything we can do to help them. It's a self-sabotage."

The caring doctor shook her head in astonishment. "Your scans... You are *upending* everything that I know."

I nodded with a confident smile. It wasn't a smug, "I told you so" smile; it was a "my God is bigger than cancer" smile, and I was happy to share it with her. She was in the beginning stages of seeing what the Lord is capable of.

No, Dr. Ibrahim. I'm not upending everything you know. He is.

"Seriously," Dr. Ibrahim leaned back in her swivel chair, a grin growing gradually at the edges of her mouth. "The fact that you have not taken your chemotherapy—the fact that you *stopped* your chemotherapy protocol only *six months* into your treatment, when it was supposed to be a *five-year treatment plan*!?... I mean, don't get me wrong. I'm *pleasantly* surprised, but I am very surprised."

Folks, just as a happy reminder of what God can do: I discontinued my chemotherapy six months in, with my final dose taken on December 31, 2021. According to science, my cancer was supposed to be back and raging throughout all my tissues somewhere between March and June of 2022. As I write this, it is March of 2024, two years past that deadly deadline.

Guess who's alive and kickin'!

January 2024: Cancer-free and, like my mug says,
living a blessed and beautiful life!

Oh, and here's a fun one: Guess who just received a phone call with some exciting news in the Western medical world? Apparently, one of the doctors in the oncology circle that I had the pleasure of discussing my treatment with heard about my story. This oncologist reached out to me recently and told me she is looking into the possibility of adding a holistic, natural-medicine branch of treatment to her own practice because of what the Lord did with me. She wants to schedule an interview with me soon. At this time, it's too early to tell if this will take off or not, but it's the beginning of *something* exciting, even if that "something" happens within that doctor's own life and faith. (Prayers are going up for that one!)

Chapter Twenty

WE ARE MADE TO SELF-REPAIR!

My God really *is* the God of healing! The God who conquers cancer and all forms of death. And what He did for me, I honestly believe He will do for anyone. I sincerely believe this healing of the Lord's is available for everyone! One thing that makes me so sad is when I hear people saying that God will heal "if it is His will." In my humble opinion, it is *always* God's will that a person be healed from this evil, disgusting disease He never made in the first place. What He did for me He can do for you or your loved one!

Now, before anyone reacts to what they've just read: I may not mean what you *think* I mean by that. There is a community of people who are guaranteed to misinterpret what I just said unless I clarify.

So often in church or in ministry gatherings, you hear teachings on miraculous healing (when it happened in the Bible, how to receive it today, etc.), and often in those cases, they're referring to something that is: 1) *only* supernatural; 2) quite sensational; and 3) requires nothing from the believer other than their faith and belief. Examples might be similar to some of the miracles Jesus performed in the New Testament: giving sight to a man who was blind since birth; untwisting a crippled man's legs who then goes leaping and dancing; raising the dead several days after they died; and so on. And when I say, "I believe God will heal *anyone* from cancer," it sounds like I might be talking about a person with an advanced stage of cancer who has been given two weeks to live receiving an instant and miraculous healing at a Christian conference, and then seeing the proof of it in scans at the doctor's office the next day: from doomed to healed in a few hours because God's touch was instant.

Do I believe those kinds of miracles and demonstrations of God's power can happen? Absolutely, yes, beyond the shadow of any doubt! I've read the New Testament, and I trust that if it says Jesus healed leprosy, boils, and open, gaping wounds, then that's just what He did, and He could do it again at any second.

However, when God spoke through Cislyn with the encouraging word that He was going to touch me, I had a lot of hours in solitary confinement in the hospital, and again later in my room, to consider all the ways that can apply. Though He certainly *could* give someone an instant touch (from doomed to healed in a few hours) I believe His will for healing some people, myself included, involves someone being obedient and faithful to *the medicine He put here specifically for our healing.*

Consider this: God's will, when He formed humanity from dust in the first place, was that the human body would be capable of healing itself, as long as we do our part in providing it the proper circumstances *for* healing. In other words, the "healing" is already in the protocol, and unless we're one of the lucky ones who do receive that instant touch at the altar, we have some responsibility on our end to reach out and take the healing protocol He has offered us, and then stick to it faithfully. For some of us, that protocol is as simple as continuing to make the same good choices we've always made, but *add to* those decisions with vitamins, supplements, exercise, and so on, so the body can meet the conditions for self-repair. For others, the protocol will require us to drop bad habits completely and *never go back* to them (smoking, eating pesticides, etc.), replacing them with good habits. But whatever the necessity, once we intentionally bring our bodies into the conditions it needs to repair itself, it will.

Already, this early on in the discussion, the question of God's will in the subject of healing has shifted from *only* having faith in an instant touch at an altar call service to *also* having faith in: 1) the body God designed at the beginning of time that is capable of self-repair, and b) the medicine He established on the earth at the beginning of time that returns the body to the conditions needed to self-repair. One might be instant and the other might take some time and effort on the believer's behalf, but both types of healing are equally real.

So, yes, I do firmly believe that it is God's will that anyone and everyone be healed just as I was, simply because it's what He already designed the body to do!

But you know what *else* God decided to instill within us when He made mankind?

Free will.

Each of us has free will, and therefore, the power to choose what will, and what *will not*, go into our body to bring it into harmony with the conditions necessary for self-repair. In my case, the requirements were to a) immediately and permanently discontinue ingesting the pesticides that I believe gave me cancer in the first place, and b) implement the natural trifecta that heals, *and maintains*, my body's optimal self-reparation. I was healed, praise the Lord and hallelujah! But, if I want to *stay* healed, I must continue to do my part and live on a clean, organic diet free of not only pesticides but animal hormones, meat treated with drugs, antibiotics, steroids, and other poisons in that seemingly bottomless pool of food additives.

Many folks might see a man dying of lung cancer after smoking for fifty years and say, "Awe, poor guy. It's so sad…but to be honest, he did it to himself. He chose those cigarettes." The same people were unlikely to look at my case and say, "Awe, poor Lynette. It's so sad…but she chose this. She ate vegetables several times a day that were sprayed with crop poisons." Why? Because the awareness levels are different. Generally, anyone that hasn't been sleeping under a rock for the last several decades can tell you, "Smoking kills." The awareness of hidden food-additive predators is much lower.

But no matter what, at the end of the day, everyone has the responsibility to be sure that what they put into their body is safe to consume, and we need to be very careful that we don't just rely on some invisible benefactors behind such organizations as the Food and Drug Administration to screen everything on our behalf. We must be willing to look for ourselves at what really lurks in that next protein bar, donut, cookie, bag of chips, or other processed food. The same goes for those ingredients that have been biologically altered with something unnatural, like beef or chicken raised on antibiotics and steroids. And as much as it pains me to point this out, it doesn't stop with food. Some of the worst toxins we can put in our body come from cosmetics, deodorants, hygiene products, perfumes, medications, etc.

Most of us have heard someone at some point ask the question, "If God is a fair and just God, then why do bad things happen to good people?" Although visiting that theological topic at length is beyond the scope and purpose of this book, if you've listened with a keen ear, very often, the "bad things" examples given by the asker include a person dying of cancer. Many of these stories involve someone who didn't deserve cancer, who truly believed God to be capable of delivering a miraculous healing, and yet, "God allowed that person to pass away anyway." This can be so very painful for those who remain to parse out. Trust me, I had an awful lot of time to think about that in the last few years. But after taking all of these things into consideration, it sheds fresh light on God's involvement. It wasn't God's will that our world would become so polluted by poisons, but it has, and we ingest them constantly, while calling *His* ingredients—like apricot kernels—dangerous or silly. A person can still ask why God allowed that tragic death, but hopefully this book has helped some folks reconsider whether all these hundreds of thousands of deaths per year in the Western world were caused by people vs. allowed by God. At the very least, I hope I have helped some answer the question: "If God is so loving, why did He create cancer."

He didn't. But what He *did* create are the ingredients to fight it, as well as to keep our blood, gut, tissues, and overall flesh clean. So, I will say it again in different words: If we want to live in a way that comes into harmony with God's will and standards for life, we must utilize our free will to ensure that what we put into our body aligns with His will and standards.

As for the individual who *does* take care of his body, who *is* willing to utilize God's medicine, and who *still* ends up going to be with the Lord as a result of some unlikely disease or condition: This issue alone could honestly justify the writing of an entire additional book, but to share at least one answer I feel particularly passionate about, consider Isaiah 57:1–2: "The righteous perisheth, and no man layeth it to heart: and merciful men are taken away, none considering that the righteous is taken away from the evil to come. He shall enter into peace: they shall rest in their beds, each one walking in his uprightness." This passage makes it clear that even the most righteous, faithful man—one who follows his convictions about God and His directives to the letter—may still be taken into His presence to remove him from future travesty or hardship. For those who remain, the list of human questions is lengthy.

We wonder why this passing occurred to one who followed all the protocols, obeyed all the rules, and made the best decisions about their health that they could with the knowledge they had. These same men who pass into the Kingdom, however, enter into eternal peace and *ultimate healing*.

Some readers might be feeling a little overwhelmed at this point, hearing that they must suddenly drop everything, learn to read labels, get to know ingredients, and understand all kinds of long words they can't pronounce, let alone understand. Let me give you a helpful hint that will shave off a *lot* of time and learning: Avoid long words you can't pronounce. Period. See that bag of beans sitting there on the shelf at the store? Pick it up and read the ingredients. If it says, "Contents: black beans," and the list stops there, that's a bingo. Organic would be the best, but if you're new at this, let your first step be to avoid the lengthy ingredients lists. Buy whole foods and teach yourself to enjoy the simple flavors of God's creation without all those unnecessary things. (It might be bland at first, especially if you're a MSG [monosodium glutamate] addict [and you might be, because it's in almost every processed food item today], but once you've purged your body of all that yuck, you'll find God's flavors are actually quite enjoyable. Humans, at one point in our history, did not have to have such additives as MSG to enjoy food, and it wouldn't be a bad idea if we got back to those simpler, cleaner days, for the sake of our collective health…and to bring the number of cancer-related deaths down substantially!)

This is all why, though I love the precious *people* within the Western system, I believe Big Pharma and the Western system is often doing more harm than good. In most cancer and chemotherapy cases (if not all), the protocol is to fight a poison-induced disease (like breast cancer brought on in part by crop pesticides) with another immunity-lowering poison (like chemotherapy). Once we take all of this into consideration for what it is, it's so sad to say it, but it's not really a surprise that cancer is one of the main causes of death in our area of the world.

Before we close the "anyone can be healed" conversation—and therefore the book with a final note from me—there is one more critical factor that should be addressed as it relates to God's will in healing anyone or everyone. That is, the patient's own will in the matter.

I know it *seems* to healthy people on the outside that Gramma Sue, Aunt Margaret, Uncle Bill, your neighbor Kelly, and anyone else with a bleak cancer prognosis would certainly want to receive healing from their cancer. Why wouldn't they? Wouldn't everyone?

Well, I have been placed in a unique position over the last couple of years to observe people of all ages and from all walks of life, and I can say this with perhaps more insight than those who maybe haven't experienced the cancer journey: You would be surprised to learn how often people are ready to go—*especially* those who are right with God and whose children are stable. These are often people who have lived long, happy, fulfilling lives. They are secure in their beliefs about where they are going next, and they believe their work here is done. Assuming they have everything in order and their children are no longer fully dependent upon them, they may just surprise you when you discover that they aren't really seeking healing at all.

I talk to people all day long who ask me for my advice or opinion on various cancer-related topics. Many times, folks will tell me they are doing everything they can for their family member or loved ones—everything from preparing healthy meals for them, to providing them with natural medicines, supporting them with prayer, and beyond. Yet, at the end of the day, the loved one either doesn't want to cooperate with the protocol, or they appear to lack interest entirely. A few times, I have gotten the feeling based on what I'm hearing that the patient doesn't want to live, so I have asked that specifically: "Have you asked your family member if they *want* to live?"

To those of us who do want to live, it might sound insane that I would ask such a thing. But again, if you lived in my shoes for the last two years, you will see people who are just tired and ready to go. If the patient is a Christian with that glorious heavenly perspective, there are perfected bodies and streets of gold on the other side, and when you're so, so, *so* tired, that all sounds like the "better place" to be, as they say. I've also suspected a couple of times that a patient is hanging on specifically for a person or a special occasion, but as soon as that loved one has accepted it or the special occasion has passed, they head on to the other side.

To a few of the women I've spoken to, I have suggested they ask the incredibly hard question of whether the patient wants to stay here, and in those cases, the patient answered no. As I suspected, they were tired and ready to be with Jesus. A couple weeks after these tough conversations, the women I spoke to called me and thanked me for being bold enough to bring this up. Their loved ones had passed peacefully, and the women who survived them had their own peace, knowing their mamas and grandmothers were ready and unafraid.

Someone once asked me the same question. It made all the difference in the world. That leads me to my final reflection, Readers...

Conclusion

THE BEST THING THAT EVER HAPPENED TO ME

I remember, when I was asked the tough question about whether I really wanted to live, it benefitted me, the patient, personally. It made me truly think about the answer to the question and identify all that I had to live *for*. This not only provided a "yes" to the question of whether I wanted to live, it also provided a "because."

...And once I had a "because," I had a reason to fight.

Hard.

As you've no doubt pieced together by now, one of the things that drove me to fight for my life harder than anything else (other than my family) was because I believed I had a ministry within me that this cancer journey was going to bring to fruition. In the beginning, I didn't know it would be a natural-healing ministry like it has become, but I knew something was in my heart somewhere, waiting to be tested, purified from its dross, and explode on the scene with a powerful statement about the power of the blood of Christ. I'm so grateful to have this ministry now clarified for me—marching orders from the Creator of the universe, pointing me to use the knowledge of a horrible season to spare others from this same kind of pain and to champion God's ingredients above the lab-created compounds that the Western authorities, themselves, call "poison." That is a reason to live if I ever needed one!

Yet, beyond a ministry, I have been given eyes to see something I had never seen before, and, as a closing thought, I would like to impart that upon you as well.

In the end, though it's quite a dramatic thing to say, cancer was the best thing that ever happened to me. When you almost leave this world before your time and then get another chance, it makes you more aware of what this gift of life is. Culture has a few pat phrases that—prior to losing all their impact through repetition and their inclusion in syrupy movie endings—captured this decently, I suppose. For instance: "Live every moment to the fullest"; "Never take anything for granted"; "Make that next moment count"; and so on. We've heard them all before, and even if they were to faithfully convey how one feels when death is narrowly escaped, they're just not big enough. It's true that you sometimes don't know how much something means to you until you lose it—so if you're lucky enough to ever get back the thing you lost, your gratitude is magnified. When *life* is the thing you lost and got back, *everything in life* is magnified, and these little cultural phrases are just pathetically insufficient for conveying the colossal magnitude of such an epiphany.

Before I got sick, I was "living." Now, I'm truly "alive"! The former inspires imagery of someone who has a pulse, while the latter infers actions taken toward a passionate life goal with a fresh perspective. It's like my appreciation for life, love, family, friends, and opportunities to connect with the lost was always there, under the surface, but cancer gave it a full exfoliation scrub, washing away all the dirt and crud that obscured me from sincerely perceiving the depth of it. With the blinders now removed, the lens I see the world through has magnified the big picture, so I can zoom in on the details in crisp, high definition, appreciating the beauty of every pixel that contributes to this lovely experience called life.

And what that does for a person's ability to love people?!

Let me try and help you see just one little pixel from *my* big picture so you can understand the enormity of what I'm communicating: When I was confined to my bed, just after my return from the hospital in late 2021, John was doing everything for me. I couldn't walk, feed myself, use the restroom, nothing. I was so weak it's a wonder I kept breathing, let alone exhibiting the strength needed to help out with my own care. I still had the C. diff infection and, though I have mostly spared readers from the specifics, those diapers John had to change on me were very disturbing. (Both blood and bacteria in a solid black "tar" stool leaves a lasting impression on one's memory.) John never once complained or said anything that would make me feel like I was gross to him or an inconvenience (and in fact, he gave me a peculiar kind of "back on the farm" reassurance—the details of which the reader would not understand unless

I described things I shouldn't), but it was obviously a lot for him to face. When he wasn't changing my diapers, he was begging God to save my life, since the last thing he saw before the soiled diapers was me, collapsing and being carted away to ICU, from which, it was said, I would not return alive.

Meanwhile, in order to keep himself sane, he would sometimes wait until my sister was with me to make a quick trip down to the local home improvement store to pick up a few things for a small project or two around the house. There at the store, standing in the checkout line, not one person ahead of him or behind him would ever know that this mild-mannered Hispanic man waiting to pay for his trinkets had just changed his wife's infected diaper. Nobody had the tiniest clue that while he was buying a bag of screws, nuts, bolts, and washers, he was secretly wishing the line would move a little faster so he could hurry back home and see if I was still alive.

The impact of this "pixel" is profound! I am so much more aware of the people around me. I have such a deeper sensitivity for the hidden pain and burdens that people carry that nobody around them will know about. That man, woman, teenager, or child right next to me at any given moment could be standing in the middle of a thunderstorm that threatens to uproot their whole life five minutes from the moment they're out of my sight. It's not enough to say, "It costs nothing to be nice," or "Being kind pays off." Those cliché sayings are just too tired to be employed here. This is big. *Every single person I come into contact with, at any moment*, may be going through something like what John faced back in those horrific days.

You never know.

And as long as you never know, you should always assume that the next smile you give to that crabby lady behind the counter at the gas station might be the reason she goes to bed that night believing she still matters to the world; the next time you give respectful eye contact to your server at a restaurant might be the crumb of confidence she needed not to let herself be taken advantage of during her blind date later that evening; the next opportunity you get to ask how someone is doing and stay for more than the one-second "fine" line we all give may be what took suicide off the table the following weekend; the next chance you have to build up that kid in the back of the class who nobody else notices may have just assisted in raising up tomorrow's Billy Graham; the next kind word you say could be that one time you impacted the life of someone like John twenty minutes after he changed his dying wife's infected diaper.

The very next moment of human interaction that you engage in—no matter how small it seems to be in your busy, hectic life—may be of paramount importance to someone else.

And this is just one teeny, tiny pixel we've zoomed in on out of the big picture. Cancer was the best thing that happened to me because it took almost dying to finally come alive. I cry when others cry and laugh when they laugh. I'm connected to *everyone* all the time. The birds don't just sing; they harmonize in worship and their song outside my window is so clear now. Food doesn't just have flavor; it explodes with it. A hug isn't a polite gesture; it's a true expression of love and concern for a fellow human being. Humming doesn't produce a tune; it creates a pulsating vibration from your chest to the world. I'm so alive now that I'm bursting with life, overflowing it outward in bucketloads onto folks around me.

See, I have also stared down the opposite, and the contrast has left its impression. I've been there: slapped with such a sudden termination of all things normal in trade for uncertainty; when my firm stance on the ground was slipping beneath me and my identity—previously built upon faith, family, habit, and a predictable sequence of everyday duties—transformed from a jovial, brightly colored exclamation point surrounded by hearts and flourishes to a cracked, broken, black question mark barely visible in the dark. I'm far more than just uniquely qualified to say I know how folks feel when they get bad news.

And I pray God will anoint this heart of mine to not only continue beating to keep my body alive, but to explode with the energy of a thousand on-fire preachers of the Gospel as I begin to minister to the hurting, to the suffering, *to the precious souls who were fed the lie that cancer is the end for them.*

Cancer is never the end. It can be the *beginning* of something, as it was for me, but it's never the end. Because, as I said in the introduction to this book: Cancer might have its own plan, but God has a better one… and His goes on forever. Meanwhile, if you *have* been handed a diagnosis, always remember: God has His own line of medication that is far, *far* stronger than you've probably been told.

The first video of mine that went viral was brought to a casual close. I never thought it would be viewed more than a handful of times, so I never planned an impressive, articulate ending. But God, in His providence, foreknew what words would best linger in the air for the viewer after the video ceased to play, and I can't think of a better way to end this book than the words He inspired me to end with once already: Speak *life*. God bless you.

Appendix A

MY PERSONAL REGIMEN

The most common question I receive from folks seeking help with their cancer situation relates to the specific regimen that helped bring healing to me, and it's one that I still follow daily. Though these steps are mentioned at length within the narrative of Chapter Sixteen: Western vs. Natural—Round Two, I chose to include it again here in concise, bullet-list fashion as a quick reference.

DISCLAIMER: As I expressed earlier in the book, these ingredients, supplements, exercises, and routines are what I believe helped bring healing to my individual stage-four, metastasized, "incurable" breast cancer, as shown through the miraculous testimony you've just read, and as I believe has been corroborated through multiple sets of blood labs and imaging scans. I trust that God led me to experience this regimen personally, and then share it with others who may be in a position to benefit from it as I have. However, I am not a doctor. Therefore: I'm not making any medical claims about any part or portion of my healing journey, nor making any assertions that the herbal medicines, supplements or lifestyle decisions I made will work for everyone or anyone else. It is vital that readers pray about their own situation, do their own research, and make their own decisions regarding their health.

I would encourage all readers to engage proactively in their own search for answers, and to seek guidance from the Great Physician who made our bodies with the capacity to self-heal in the first place. Beyond that, I encourage you to be consistent on your routine of treatment—whatever that regimen may be for you. And remember, a "treatment," "regimen," or "protocol" is not only made up of what medicine or supplements you swallow; it involves a consistent lifestyle made up of good rest; a healthy, clean diet, free of harmful chemicals and additives; regular exercise behaviors; and keeping a watchful eye out to recognize what other toxicities you may be exposed to at your job, around home, in your housecleaning products, hygiene or cosmetic products, and so on. We cannot engage in destructive behavior in one area of our lives and expect our general health not to somehow reflect that decision in some way.

First, I will take a moment to remind readers of the three key supplements that are central to my personal regimen, as well as provide some guiding notes to help folks identify a quality product should they wish to do any follow up research on any part of this regimen on their own.

Please note that these ingredients should always be from the absolute cleanest and most organic sources. It doesn't make sense to feed an immunocompromised body with poisonous pesticides or genetically modified—and therefore entirely unnatural—organisms. It is so vital that, as we fortify our body via plants rich in "the good guys," we are not simultaneously injuring it by letting "the bad guys" sneak through.

1. **Soursop leaves:** Though these leaves are available dried, ground, and placed in convenient tea bags, there are a number of reasons I would suggest avoiding this format. First, though very few people are aware of this, tea bags are actually quite toxic. Whether they are paper, plastic, nylon, or something else, tea bags are often treated with all sorts of chemicals, hormones, nanoplastics, nitrates, aluminums, etc. that absolutely *do* leach out into your tea water, and it's too easy for tea companies to sneak in other leaves or filler into the mix, keeping you from receiving the unadulterated, pure soursop leaf medicine beneficial to your body. I opt for either whole organic leaves, as they are large and easy to scoot around the water, so you don't have to mess with dregs, or even more specifically crushed loose-leaf format because more nutrients are released during the boiling process.

2. **Black seed oil** (also called "black cumin seed oil"): This product must be cold pressed, vegan, and again, non-GMO. A "cold-press" extraction method means that the oil obtained was never exposed to the high temperatures that effectively cancel or "cook out" the natural health benefits. Additionally, check the extraction process on the specific oil you're considering to ensure that no other ingredients or solvents (such as hexane) were used in its making.
3. **Apricot kernels:** In addition to being organic, these must be raw and unsweetened. If they have been sweetened, roasted, or cooked in any way, two concerns arise: 1) the roasting, cooking, and sweetening processes will burn out or cancel many of the inherent disease-fighting nutrients that drew you to apricot kernels in the first place; 2) cancer feeds on sugar; apricot kernels that have been sweetened not only introduce an all-you-can-eat-buffet of sugar that keeps cancer strong and well-fed, unnecessary sugar in the blood will weaken an immune system further and lower the body's ability to fight illness. If you want to avoid sabotaging the health-restoring, cancer-fighting attributes of the kernels, stick with raw and unsweetened. (For more information regarding apricot kernels, their rich vitamin b17 content, and the impact that has upon cancer cells, consider obtaining a copy of *World Without Cancer: The Story of Vitamin B17* by G. Edward Griffin. This book took into consideration thousands of medical studies, and is, at the time of this writing, rated as "#1 Best Seller" in the "Nursing Oncology" category within one of the most popular bookstores in the world.)

In addition to taking these supplements, I will share the following habits, which became my non-negotiables while I pursued natural healing.

As for my diet: I will not eat anything with added sugars, or processed foods (like fast foods, microwave foods, etc.). It is super important to eat foods high in fiber, as that helps to move food out of your body. (Waste that sits in the body more than about a day increases the risk of toxicity, as the body will begin to re-absorb this material.) When I'm in need of a snack, I often eat raw nuts of any kind. Occasionally I will have a small portion of raisins, but I'm careful not to eat much at once because the natural sugars can get a little high. Overall, I avoid any foods that have more than two ingredients unless I am familiar with what those ingredients are.

Over the course of the day, I drink eight, 9 oz glasses of clean water. In one of these, I add ¼ tsp. of baking soda and three drops of food-grade hydrogen peroxide (which is tasteless). (Baking soda alkalizes the water, which in turn alkalizes the body. For the most part, illness, disease, and cancer struggle more to survive in an alkaline-body like they can in acidic bodies. There are a number of other benefits as well, such as cleansing the kidneys, suppressing acid indigestion, assistance with urinary tract infections, etc. The food-grade hydrogen peroxide delivers oxygen to the cells, and of course, an oxygenated body is a healthier body, but that is only the beginning. There have been tens of thousands of documented reports listing food-grade hydrogen peroxide as effective supports to help treat many conditions, ailments, and diseases. Many other countries use this amazing, inexpensive aid as a common medicine, as well as a key ingredient in their protocols for cancer, heart disease, autoimmune diseases, and more. For more information on that, consider the book *The One-Minute Cure* by Madison Cavanaugh.)

As noted briefly prior: What is put *on* the body can be as important as what is put *in* the body. Purity of everything we consume is vital for our health. As such, I now avoid lotion and deodorants. To care for my skin, I use castor oil mixed with water. If a deodorant is needed, baking soda may offer a good alternative.

One item that is not given a single specific time or routine—*but is the absolute most important habit to form in any journey toward healing of any kind*—is prayer. I made it a point to pray each day, making specific mention of a list of things I am grateful for, including my health and my village of supporters.

Morning:

- Before getting out of bed, I stretch my entire body thoroughly. This helps me feel refreshed as I get out of bed and helps my circulation.

- Immediately upon rising, I drink 6 oz of water with lemon.
- I then eat one raw, unsweetened, organic apricot kernel.
- In my soursop tea, I use a teaspoon of crushed, loose-leaf soursop in 16 oz of boiled water. (During my healing journey, I used to place five or six full soursop leaves in 32 oz of boiling water—half of which I drank in the morning and the other half I consumed in the evening.) The color of the soursop tea can vary from golden yellow, to brown, to dark green.
- While I am waiting for the soursop to steep, I take one teaspoon of vegan, cold-pressed black seed oil.
- Then comes my thirty minutes of sunlight, directly on my skin from the great outdoors. Whenever possible, I take my shoes off and feel the earth beneath my feet. (As a reminder: This is called "grounding" or "earthing," in case you want to look it up and read about all the benefits for yourself.)
- Returning to the indoors, I drink my first 16 oz cup of soursop tea.
- For breakfast, I will often make a plain omelet from the eggs I collect from my chickens (which are obviously cage-free and organic). I season it lightly with cayenne pepper, turmeric and pure sea salt. I always have fruit with my food, and sometimes I opt for a lighter breakfast, choosing to eat only fruit.

Midday/Early Afternoon:

- My afternoon begins with another raw, unsweetened, organic apricot kernel,
- For lunch, I often eat a fruit and veggie salad. I personally choose to mix these with no dressing, as I have learned to enjoy the blend of the natural flavors. Sometimes, using an organic, healthy olive oil or avocado oil, I fry a small, palm-size piece of organic chicken or wild-caught fish to go with it. (I generally eat meat once or twice a week.)
- Once again, I go outside for more sunlight on my face. In the afternoon, I like to get some exercise, which manifests into some light tussling or running around with my dogs. Sometimes I will do some light gardening, as this is another

nice source of moderate exercise. (Exercise is a *vital* part of a healthy lifestyle, as it helps to move the lymphatic system, which is the drainage system of your body, so you *do* want to implement this into your routine when your body is strong enough. However, don't assume every single exercise session has to be a big sweaty, huffy-puffy, cardio-explosion. That's wonderful if you're very strong, fit, and healthy, but to those who are ill or recovering from cancer: Go easy on yourself. You are healing! Ask your doctor, trainer, certified holistic practitioner, or equivalent what level of exercise *you should personally* be engaging in.)

- Although I do have a literal tiny prayer chapel John built me, prior to that, I considered the outdoors to be my prayer room, where I would go to have a session with the Most High. "Outside" can be the prettiest church! I make time for prayer at other times of the day as well.

Evening:

- I eat another kernel of apricot, take one teaspoon of black seed oil, and then drink my second 16 oz serving of soursop tea, which also helps me sleep because of its effects on insomnia.
- For dinner, I generally eat whatever I feel like having, so long as it is something God created.
- Although I still allow myself to grab a drink any time of day I'm thirsty, I stop eating at seven o'clock in the evening, so: 1) my body can slip into intermittent fasting mode; 2) my liver can detox; 3) my digestive system can rest from food consumption.
- Lastly, I make sure to get eight full, uninterrupted hours of sleep every night.

To anyone who may find this information helpful, I personally use many of the health supplements, as well as the hygiene and personal care products, from EdensEssentials.com, because they are made of the highest-quality, pure, organic ingredients and ethically sourced.

Appendix B

TESTIMONIALS

The following are only a few testimonials I have received from folks who reached out to me after my first video went viral. My heart swells for these precious people, and I would like to include their statements both as a way to celebrate their achievements alongside them, as well as to encourage others who might just be entering the natural-healing arena.

(Though names have been changed for privacy, and typos common to social-media network conversations have been edited and language smoothed, the spirit behind these comments has not been altered.)

> "I have been taking soursop and black seed oil, and eating three apricot kernels per day, for a little over three months now. I had metastasized cancer, clustered primarily in my arms and shoulder area. When my doctor took follow-up scans at a recent appointment, he announced that I am now cancer-free!"—BoostedRider

> "I started on apricot seeds back in mid-May. Today, in late June, my PET scan showed my tumor has begun to shrink. I think this is working!"—SunglassesIndoors

> "Thanks to you, Lynette, and to God of course, the doctor says the lumps in my breasts are gone after taking apricot seeds, soursop tea, and black seed oil!"—Vicki

> "Hello Lynette. Because of *you*, I started taking apricot seeds and soursop tea, and now—drumroll please!—I am cancer-free! Thank you so much for being willing to speak about these natural healing methods despite the risk."—BrunetteInLove

"Lynette, my dear friend, I owe you a mountain of gratitude. Had it not been for *you*, I wouldn't have ever known there was a natural treatment for cancer. I've been taking what you've been taking, but I also added in the turkey tail mushrooms. And the report? Blurry spots on the scans are clearing up and improving, while breast cancer scans were negative! Looks like I'm not going to need surgery! On the other hand, I'm not counting my chickens before they hatch; I will continue the protocol and continue the fight. I would love to hear from you; please give me a call at [###-###-####]!"—NaturalArizonaGal

"I will never be able to thank you enough for speaking up and sharing your story. With your help, my brother's life was spared. After his abdominal cancer diagnosis, he began a regimen of black seed oil, soursop tea leaves, and apricot kernels, just like you said in the video. His cancer is GONE! It literally doesn't exist anymore."—SpikeySimpson

"Lynette, I have wonderful news! Praise the Lord, I just got my scans back, just before Halloween—all is benign! Please let me know if you continue the protocol even after the scare is over. Thanks!"—BraidsAndBrownEyes

"I love Lynette's natural approach. My son's tumor is shrinking as we speak! It's a complete and total miracle of God!"—ItalianMama

"My Cancer Antigen (CA-125) test was more than three times above normal at just under 120. Doctors were discussing some very dramatic, irreversible, and highly invasive surgeries. I started first on prayer and soursop, and then I added in the apricot seeds. Four weeks later, my CA-125 marker was barely above 15! My doctor doesn't know what to do with me or my treatment, because he's just so shocked. He made me take the blood tests twice just to be sure he was really seeing what he thought he was, and now the CA-125 markers are all the way down to 5!"—BritishCitizen

"Mildred's tumor is totally disappeared! This is because of God's medicine! Praise be to the Lord!"—PeachBubbles

"Glad to have found you on here, girl; I love hearing what you have to say about all this natural healing. I plan to share all your videos with two more people this week who have been diagnosed with cancer. Last fall, I shared your videos and supplement protocols with one friend who, just after that, started taking soursop, black seed oil, and apricot kernels, and she is healed from her pancreatic cancer! The chemotherapy was on a path to killing her (and she had absolutely no energy and felt awful all the time), and now she looks great and feels happy! She told her doctor she didn't want to be on chemotherapy anymore, and he asked her what she was taking instead. When she told him about the natural protocol, he acted as if he already knew about it and already knew it would work! Anyway, I'm watching all your videos on Rumble! Much love!"—AnonymousHearts

"Hello, Ma'am! Thanks for all your reminders and help! Dad and I have stopped relying on the juices and switched to soursop tea last January. We were praying that his Prostate-Specific Antigen (PSA) numbers would be normal and, as of today, he is cancer-free! We are still using the apricot kernels and soursop. Thank you so much for being open with your journey!"—SwankyBleach

"Hello pretty lady! Just checking in to tell you that my last two appointments have rendered cancer-free results since I've changed the protocol, praise the Lord! Looking forward to catching your next live video and joining you in your fasting. Trust God with me that this good news will remain. Hugs!"—BlackBasketWeave

Endnotes

1 "Chemotherapy." Under "Side Effects." *National Institute of Health.* Accessed March 3, 2024, https://www.nhsinform.scot/tests-and-treatments/non-surgical-procedures/chemotherapy/; emphasis added.

2 Marcus, Ben. "Chemotherapy is Poison. No, Literally." Published August 24, 2020. *Illinois Science Council.* Accessed March 3, 2024, https://www.illinoisscience.org/blog/chemotherapy-is-poison/; emphasis added.

3 "Chemotherapy safety." *American Cancer Society.* Accessed March 3, 2024, https://www.cancer.org/cancer/managing-cancer/treatment-types/chemotherapy/chemotherapy-safety.html.

4 Curtis, L. "What is Turkey Tail?" December 23, 2022. *Very Well Health.* Accessed January 29, 2024, https://www.verywellhealth.com/turkey-tail-mushroom-6890534.

5 WebMD, "Turkey Tail Mushroom—Uses, Side Effects, and More," 2024, Accessed January 29, 2024, https://www.webmd.com/vitamins/ai/ingredientmono-648/turkey-tail-mushroom.

6 Amit, D., Swain, R., Belonce, S., & Jacobs, R. J. (2023). "Therapeutic Effects of Medicinal Mushrooms on Gastric, Breast, and Colorectal Cancer: A Scoping Review." *Cureus,* 15(4), e37574. Accessed January 29, 2024. https://doi.org/10.7759/cureus.37574.

7 Ali, S. A., Parveen, N., & Ali, A. S. (2018). Links between the Prophet Muhammad (PBUH) recommended foods and disease management: A review in the light of modern superfoods. *International journal of health sciences, 12*(2), 61–69.

8 Khan, M. A., Chen, H. C., Tania, M., & Zhang, D. Z. (2011). Anticancer activities of Nigella sativa (black cumin). *African journal of traditional, complementary, and alternative medicines: AJTCAM, 8*(5 Suppl), 226–232. Accessed January 30, 2024, https://doi.org/10.4314/ajtcam.v8i5S.10.

9 Stuart, A. 2024. "Graviola, Soursop." *Herbal Safety.* Accessed January 30, 2024, https://www.utep.edu/herbal-safety/herbal-facts/herbal%20facts%20sheet/soursop.html#:~:text=Some%20studies%20have%20shown%20that,potential%20for%20treating%20gastric%20ulcers.

10 Sachdev, P. 2022, "Health Benefits of Soursop," *WebMD.* Accessed January 30, 2024, https://www.webmd.com/food-recipes/health-benefits-soursop.

11 Hasan AEZ, Julistiono H, Bermawie N, Riyanti EI, Arifni FR. "Soursop leaves (*Annona muricata* L.) endophytic fungi anticancer activity against HeLa cells." Saudi J Biol Sci. 2022 Aug; 29 (8):103354. Accessed March 15, 2024, https://www.ncbi.nlm.nih.gov/pmc/articles/PMC9256652/; doi: 10.1016/j.sjbs.2022.103354. Epub 2022 Jun 21. PMID: 35813114; PMCID: PMC9256652.

12 Mutakin M, Fauziati R, Fadhilah FN, Zuhrotun A, Amalia R, Hadisaputri YE. "Pharmacological Activities of Soursop (*Annona muricata* Lin.)." Molecules. 2022

Feb 10;27(4):1201. Accessed March 15, 2024, https://www.ncbi.nlm.nih.gov/pmc/articles/PMC8878098/; emphasis added; doi: 10.3390/molecules27041201. PMID: 35208993; PMCID: PMC8878098.

13 Saleh, MD, MS, Naveed. "Common OTC drugs that carry serious health risks." Published March 9, 2021. *MDLinx*. Accessed January 30, 2024, https://www.mdlinx.com/article/common-otc-drugs-that-carry-serious-health-risks/5G2nI0LWR2MlQ4W2j6BS0b#.

14 Akhone, M. A., Bains, A., Tosif, M. M., Chawla, P., Fogarasi, M., & Fogarasi, S. (2022). Apricot Kernel: Bioactivity, Characterization, Applications, and Health Attributes. *Foods (Basel, Switzerland)*, *11*(15), 2184. https://doi.org/10.3390/foods11152184.

15 Ibid.

STAY CONNECTED!

For additional testimonials and stories of success; helpful information concerning natural, plant-based medicines from God's Creation not otherwise covered in this book; adjustments I make to my regimen as I continue to grow and gain knowledge in the most optimal, ideal, and thriving post-cancer life; as well as details regarding how to connect with me through social media or contact me for potential speaking opportunities: Please visit my website at **www.SpeakerLynette.com**.